THRUST FOR F

A 'Without Formulae' Book

THRUST FOR FLIGHT

W. THOMSON
B.Sc., E.Eng., M.I.Mech.E., A.F.R.Ae.S

SECOND EDITION
Updated by Bill Gunston

Longman Scientific & Technical,
Longman Group UK Limited,
Longman House, Burnt Mill, Harlow,
Essex CM20 2JE, England
and Associated Companies throughout the world.

First published 1969
First paperback edition 1972
Second edition 1992

British Library Cataloguing in Publication Data
A catalogue record for this book is available from the British Library.

ISBN 0-582-08280-3

Set by 3 in Linotype Times 10/11

Produced by Longman Group (FE) Limited
Printed in Hong Kong

CONTENTS

Because of the diversity of information that has to be given and the fact that there is some overlapping in the theory of piston engines and turbines, it has been considered advisable to divide the book into sections rather than cut it into chapters which would tend to segregate the items over-much. The list of contents and the index at the end of the book should enable subjects to be located quite readily when required.

The Plates are positioned at the end of the book

PREFACE TO SECOND EDITION

This book was written as a companion to *Flight Without Formulae*, which is concerned with the flight of aeroplanes. In 1989 this appeared in a Fifth Edition which I was pleased to update. I left the original text completely unaltered, but merely added numerous comments and updates, plus an extra section to bring this classic work up to date, and a new set of plates at the back.

I am grateful to Longman for asking me to update *Thrust for Flight*. In this case, however, there was no practical way of leaving the original text untouched. Instead large parts have been completely rewritten, because the technology of engines has changed even more completely than the way aeroplanes fly. This procedure was made easier by the fact that the entire text had to be reset anyway, so no extra costs were thereby incurred. I also took it upon myself to suggest changes to several of the figures.

As before, the update is completed by a new extra section, plus a fresh set of illustrations. If one tries to be up to date, in a field of technology subject to rapid advances, the result very quickly looks out of date. Some of the illustrations in this new edition are of things not yet built, but in 20 years' time it will still be possible to deduce – hopefully not with scorn – that this edition was done in about 1992. I wish I could include photographs taken in the year 2000, but that's difficult!

1992

Bill Gunston

PREFACE TO FIRST EDITION

This book was written as a companion volume to *Flight Without Formulae* and other similar works in this series. The success of these earlier publications shows that there is a need for books which deal with technical subjects without the formality of the normal textbook and without recourse to mathematics. Sometimes the use of a formula can reduce the labour of explaining some abstruse point, but the same short cut may only serve to sidetrack those readers to whom formulae are either a bore or a mystery. Even amongst engineers with some mathematical ability the author found that formal proofs were much more acceptable if the facts were already understood. For example, if a young engineer has already come to understand the advantages to be gained by the use of high compression ratios he is much more likely to take an interest in the same fact as it is revealed by a mathematical proof.

When the suggestion was first made that this book should be written it seemed to offer an easy way of filling in the first few months of retirement by stringing together the vast array of notes that had accumulated during a lifetime's interest in the internal combustion engine. Only after several abortive attempts and much study of the technique used in other works in the series did the book begin to take its present shape. Originally the subject matter was presented in more or less chronological order with separate sections for piston engines and turbines, but now propulsion comes first for that is what the book is about and the other subjects follow when needed to enlarge on the original theme. Wherever possible explanations are provided but here and there certain basic facts have had to be given without any argument to support them.

Considerable effort has gone into making the diagrams as simple as possible, shorn of nuts and bolts or any other paraphernalia likely to obscure the issue even if very vital in practice.

Further illustrations are given in the collection of photographs gathered together in a separate section at the end of the book. Each photograph has been fully captioned so that it is possible to browse through the pictorial section without having to turn back to the text to find out what it is all about.

It is with pleasure that I put on record my appreciation of the help given by a number of manufacturers in the aircraft industry who have provided photographs, brochures and information needed in compiling this book. A great deal of information has also been gleaned over the years from the journals and proceedings of the Institution of Mechanical Engineers and of the Royal Aeronautical Society. To any reader anxious to widen his knowledge of internal combustion engines these sources of information are strongly recommended – the reading is not exactly light but the subject is surely one that warrants some careful thought.

The help given by the following is acknowledged with thanks—

Bristol Engine Division of Rolls-Royce
Dowty Group Limited
Henry Wiggin & Company Limited
Lucas Gas Turbine Equipment Limited
Rolls-Royce Limited
Ultra Electronics Limited

1969

W.T.

THRUST FOR FLIGHT

1. The Need for Thrust

Throughout the history of aviation progress has depended on the availability of suitable engines. Even the simplest of aircraft needs thrust to be applied to launch it from the ground and keep it airborne if it is to follow a prescribed flight plan. Gliders may appear to be engineless but how many of them get off the ground without the help of a tow rope? Even after the initial launching the pilot can only exercise a very limited amount of control and the glider is very much at the mercy of the elements. There can be little doubt that for serious scheduled flight thrust must be applied for most of the time the aircraft is in the air.

Motor-cars, railway trains and similar vehicles propel themselves by forcing their wheels to rotate on the surface of the road or rail which provides something solid to push against. Even the action of walking depends on the ability to apply forces with the feet. On a very slippery surface, when the forces cannot be applied properly, movement is uncertain and perhaps hazardous. But if two people standing on a smooth icy surface push against one another, they will slide apart, that is both of them will move but in opposite directions. This is the principle on which ships and aircraft depend for their propulsion – to move forward they must somehow get a hold on the medium in which they float or fly and force it behind them in sufficient quantities and at such speeds that a worthwhile force is applied.

2. Forces on an Aircraft in Flight

When an aircraft is in steady horizontal flight the thrust required from the propulsion system is equal to the drag which acts on the aircraft as a result of its motion through the air. The resistance to be overcome depends on many things, but the main items are the drag which is associated with the lifting force generated by the wings, turbulence set up by the aircraft as it moves through the air and, to some extent, the friction between the moving air and the panels of the aircraft. When an aircraft is required to climb or to accelerate, the demands for thrust become greater. The problems now are how to provide it economically and in the quantities required.

3. Propellers and Jet Propulsion

Two main propulsion systems are recognized: those that use propellers to force the air back, and those that use what has come to be known as jet propulsion. Both depend on exactly the same principle and get their forward thrust by forcing air out at the back of the system – the only difference is in the way the air is handled. When the various systems are examined closely it will be seen that they overlap considerably. Piston engines which generate thrust by driving propellers may also exert considerable thrust at suitably proportioned and suitably directed exhaust stubs, and the air which is heated in the cooling system may contribute thrust because of the energy given to it. When a turbine is used to drive a propeller there is an obvious combination of both forms of propulsion. All the many attempts to combine piston engines with turbines or jet propulsion have ended in failure (though superchargers driven by turbines spun by the exhaust from a piston engine are very important). Today we have a continuous spectrum of gas-turbine engines, ranging from the turboprop (see PROPELLER in Fig. 1) through propfans and turbofans to the turbojet. Today the turbojet is used only for simple trainers and target drones, and a few supersonic aircraft.

4. Propellers, Jets and Rockets Compared

The various propulsion systems represent the same principle applied in a variety of ways, ranging from the propeller at one extreme to the rocket at the other. Assuming it were possible to get a range of systems each giving exactly the same thrust it would be found that the differences lay in the mass of air handled and in the change of speed applied to it. The propeller handles a relatively large mass of air to which is given a moderate increase in speed whereas the rocket uses a very small quantity of gas but imparts to it a really enormous increase in speed. For the same thrust the jet engine handles less air than the propeller (but more than the rocket) and gives it a higher velocity (but not nearly as high as that given by the rocket).

5. Source of Thrust

In every case the thrust has come somehow or other as a result of burning fuel and using the heat released to give the air or gases the high velocities from which the thrust is derived. Since there is fuel involved, it is only natural to count the cost and find out how effi-

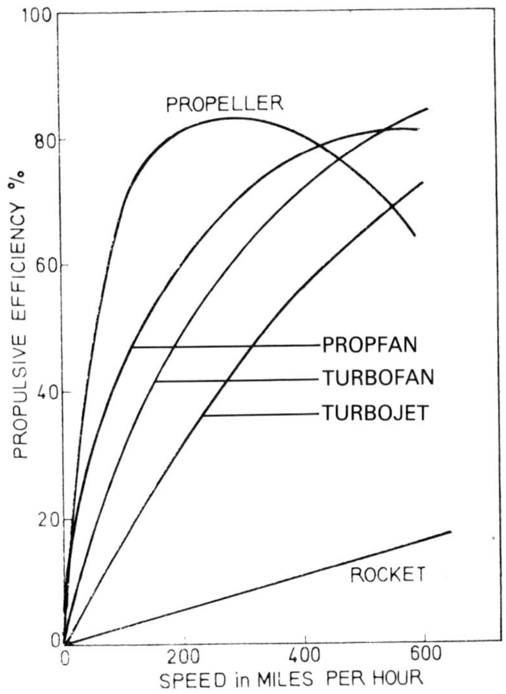

Fig. 1 Propulsive efficiencies

ciently the fuel has been used to speed up the air and whether the energy so given to the air has been altogether usefully employed.

When a vehicle is driven over a road there is no disturbance of the road surface and nearly all the energy expended is used in moving the vehicle. Propulsion in a fluid (air is a fluid) is different, for when an aircraft is in flight there is a tremendous commotion behind it because the air must be driven to the rear to give forward thrust. This moving air left behind by the aircraft has kinetic energy (energy of motion) which is of no further use after it leaves the aircraft. Such losses are inevitable when a fluid has to be used for propulsion but correct matching of the speed of the jet of air and the aircraft speed can make the most of the energy available.

6. Efficient Propulsion in a Fluid

Readers with some knowledge of mechanics will know that the thrust depends on the mass of fluid moved and on the change of velocity given to the fluid, whereas the kinetic energy in the slipstream depends on the mass of air and on the square of the velocity. For this reason a system giving a small increase in velocity to a large mass of air has less kinetic energy going to waste than an alternative system obtaining the same thrust with a smaller mass of air and a much higher velocity. When efficient propulsion is of major importance as a means of keeping down fuel costs and giving the maximum range for a given weight of fuel lifted from the ground at take-off, the designer's aim will always be to get the required thrust with a low jet velocity and he has to exercise his ingenuity to get the necessary flow of air through the propulsion system. Fig. 1 shows an interesting comparison of propulsive efficiencies for propeller, jet and rocket. An exact definition of propulsive efficiency is not necessary at this stage provided it is realized that the efficiency is tied up with the kinetic energy that remains in the air or exhaust gases after they leave the aircraft. A low propulsive efficiency can be taken to mean that there is considerable kinetic energy in the slipstream compared with the energy actually used to propel the aircraft.

The important thing to notice from Fig. 1 is that the propeller is very much more efficient than either the pure jet or the rocket at speeds below 300 m.p.h. and that its efficiency lessens seriously at speeds above 450 m.p.h., whereas that of the jet engine and the rocket continue to improve. The very low propulsive efficiency of the rocket must not be taken to mean that this device is not a powerful one – the reverse is true – but because of the low propulsive efficiency it is a costly one to operate. Rockets are not dealt with in any detail in this book because they are seldom employed as main engines in aircraft. Rockets are discussed briefly in the following section, with particular emphasis on the American Space Shuttle.

7. Rockets

Unlike piston engines and turbines, rockets do not consume atmospheric air to support their combustion and obtain their thrust; instead, chemical reactions (of which burning is one) are relied upon to produce the supply of hot gases used to obtain propulsion. This independence of the atmosphere is essential when the thrust is needed in space or at very high altitudes, but it has the drawback that tankage must be provided for the oxidant, or its equivalent, as well as the fuel. Some rockets burn a mixture of kerosene and hydrogen peroxide whilst others, for special applications, consume substances with greater capacity for heat release.

It is a feature of rockets that enormous thrusts may be generated considering the small size and weight of the engine, but the duration of the thrust is limited because of the very heavy fuel consumption involved. Plate 1 shows a typical large manned aerospace application. The Shuttle Orbiter has three SSMEs (Space Shuttle Main Engines), each with a single thrust chamber burning liquid hydrogen and liquid oxygen (Plate 1). At the standard 104 per cent rated power, which is maintained for 519 seconds (over 8.5 minutes) from liftoff, these propellants are pumped at the rate of 21,700 gallons per minute, by pumps rated at 23,600 h.p. for oxygen and 69,100 h.p. for hydrogen, to give a thrust of 488,800 lb (all these figures are for each engine). Each SSME is maintained by airline procedures, for 55 flights between overhauls.

Small rockets giving perhaps 1,000 lb thrust are sometimes used to assist the takeoff of aircraft at very hot high-altitude airfields. The practice is not widespread because of its high cost.

8. Aerofoils

Aircraft wings and the blades of propellers, compressors and turbines have one thing in common – they are all *aerofoils*; that is, they are designed to deflect air in such a way as to develop some desired force, which is thrust in the case of propellers and lift in the case of wings. This useful function must be performed with the least possible disturbance to the airflow, as turbulence causes drag and this in turn requires power to overcome it. Aerofoils vary somewhat in shape depending on what they have to do and on how fast they are expected to travel. Some are cambered, or curved, as in the case of compressor and turbine blades, while others, like that shown in Fig. 2 are biconvex. When any aerofoil section is placed at a small angle to a smoothly flowing stream of air (it does not matter whether it is the aerofoil or the air that moves) a favourable pressure distribution is created around it and an upward force R is applied to the aerofoil. In the case of the propeller blade there are two components of the force R which are of vital importance: the *thrust*, acting parallel to the propeller shaft, and the *drag* which resists rotation.

9. Optimum Angle of Attack

As the angle between the aerofoil and the relative airflow is increased, the resultant force R increases and with it both the thrust and the drag increase also. At one angle, known as the *optimum angle of attack*, the ratio of thrust to drag is a maximum and this

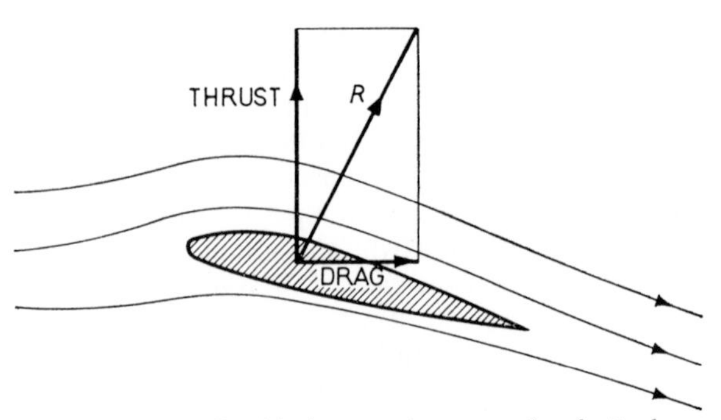

Fig. 2 Propeller blade at optimum angle of attack

represents the best bargain in terms of pounds of thrust per pound of drag. If the angle of attack is made too large in an attempt to get the greatest possible thrust, flow becomes turbulent and the blade is said to be *stalled*. In this condition (Fig. 3) most of the energy supplied to the blade is used up in producing eddies and very little is available to give thrust.

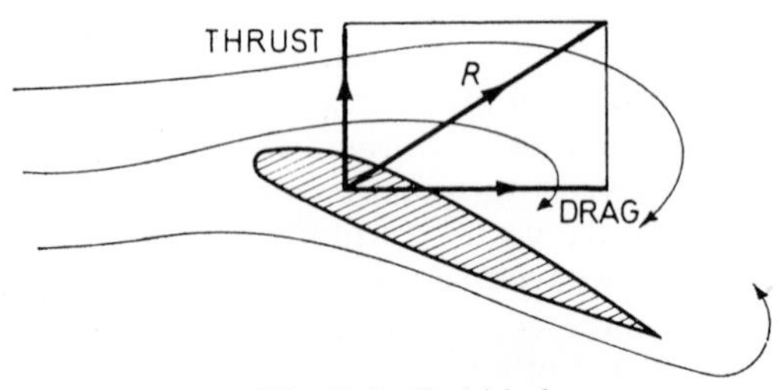

Fig. 3 Stalled blade

10. Propeller Blades

When the aerofoil is used as a propeller blade the velocity at which the airflow meets any section of the blade is made up of two components, one the forward speed of the aircraft and the other the speed due to rotation (Fig. 4). If every section throughout the length of the blade is to meet the airflow at the optimum angle of attack the blade must be twisted because the component due to rotation increases from root to tip. Thus, the root of the blade must have an extremely coarse pitch, the aerofoil being almost parallel to the propeller shaft, while the tip has to be at a very fine pitch, almost at right-angles to the propeller shaft (it also has to be much thinner).

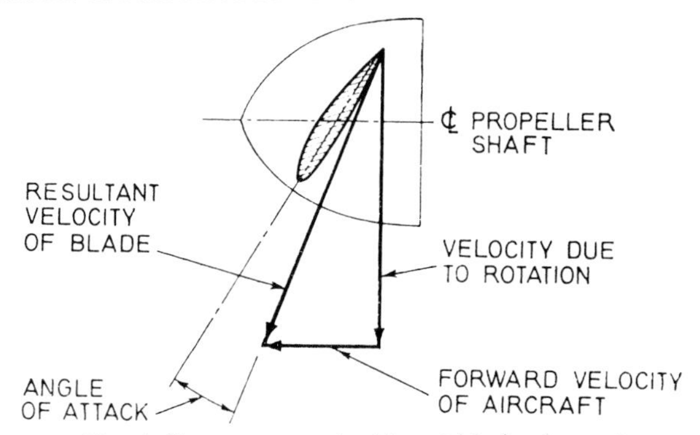

Fig. 4 Component velocities at blade element

11. Variable-Pitch and Constant-Speed Propellers

Except those for simple aeroplanes, such as microlights, modern propellers have blades which can be rotated about a radial axis and positioned in flight so as to work as nearly as possible at the optimum angle of attack throughout the speed range. At low forward speeds the blade sections make very small angles with the plane of rotation and are said to be in *fine pitch.* As forward speed increases the angle must be increased to give a *coarser pitch* to accommodate the larger forward speed component. Control of the pitch angle is done automatically so as to keep the speed of rotation constant; any tendency for the speed to drop is countered by changing to a finer pitch to reduce the drag, and vice versa. Some details are given in Section 19 to show how typical variable-pitch and constant-speed mechanisms work.

12. Feathering

If an engine is stopped for any reason that does not call for an immediate restart the blades are rotated beyond the coarse pitch position until they are edge on to the airflow. In this position there is the minimum drag to be overcome by the other engines, and there is no tendency to rotate the propeller shaft with the risk of causing further damage to an engine which may have been stopped because of a mechanical failure.

13. Reversible-Pitch Propellers

On some installations it is possible to move the blades beyond the fine pitch position until they are actually trying to drive the air forward and oppose the motion of the aircraft, a setting used to reduce the landing run after the aircraft has touched down. Braking by reversed propeller thrust avoids wear on the tyres and brakes, and is particularly welcome on wet or icy runways.

14. Blade-Tip Speed

Determination of blade diameter and speed of rotation is tied up with how fast the blade tip is moving. The blade is an aerofoil, and like its big brother the aircraft wing it requires enormous power to force it through the air once the speed of sound is reached. At this speed, and beyond it, the blade no longer moves smoothly through the air without disturbing it seriously. Instead of flowing smoothly over the blade section the air is compressed with the formation of shock waves and the absorption of a tremendous amount of energy. As this phenomenon occurs again and again with high speed aircraft when performance is stretched to the limit, some knowledge of its significance is necessary for an appreciation of the nature of the problems which come with it.

The flow pattern shown in Fig. 2 is based on the fact that in low-speed flight the air behaves as if it is incompressible. Demonstrations in smoke tunnels and in water channels show that when an object moves through a fluid at any speed below the speed of sound a warning of some sort goes out ahead of it and prepares the air for the passage of the object. This 'preparation' is given by pressure waves which move out in all directions at the speed of sound. When a body is moving at or above the speed of sound, no warning of its approach can be sent ahead of it. If the air cannot be warned of the approaching object it will not be deflected out of the way and the object will strike it violently. The air is compressed and forms a shock wave behind which the speed is lower and the pressure higher. Fig. 5 shows

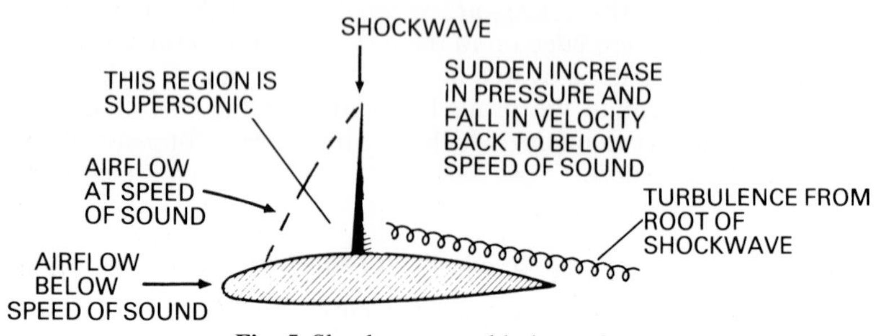

Fig. 5 Shock wave on blade section

the application of this idea to a propeller blade section which is travelling at a speed just below that of sound. As the air travels over the curved surface of the blade its speed increases for reasons that will become clearer as study proceeds in those sections of the book that are concerned with energy changes in convergent and divergent passages. In this case the speed of sound is reached at a point nearly half-way along the section. A shock wave is formed and the curved surface of the blade is exposed to a higher pressure than would exist under normal flight conditions at a lower speed. This increased pressure resists both the rotation of the propeller and the motion of the aircraft and demands extremely high powers if speed is to be maintained. From the point of view of converting shaft power to thrust, these conditions are very uneconomic.

The existence of the shock can be demonstrated by optical means which make use of the change in air density at the point where compression takes place. The wave is sometimes visible above the wings of high-speed aircraft when the pressure changes produce sudden condensation of atmospheric moisture at the point where the speed of sound is reached.

15. Propeller Reduction Gears

In the early days propellers were mounted directly on the crankshaft, and this as well as other mechanical considerations dictated the maximum speed at which the engine could be run if excessive blade tip speeds were to be avoided. This straightforward arrangement is still acceptable on light aircraft with power requirements below about 300 h.p. but when higher powers are needed some alternative must be found to increasing the engine size and weight. Increasing the engine speed is an attractive proposition, for all other things being equal, higher engine speeds mean more power strokes per minute and more power. Unfortunately 'all other things' are not equal, but if the engine is mechanically strong enough to withstand the higher stresses and if the cooling system can cope with the extra heat which has to be dissipated, running the engine faster may give extra power with very little extra weight. So that the propeller is not forced to run at excessive speed a reduction gear must be placed between the crankshaft and the propeller shaft. This, of course, introduces a weight penalty but sometimes a fast-running engine with a reduction gear can be made lighter than a direct-drive engine of equal power. On piston engines the propeller usually runs at about half the speed of the crankshaft but in turboprops much higher reductions are necessary because of the high turbine r.p.m.

16. Number of Blades Required

The thrust handled by a blade depends on the pressures applied to it and on the blade area. When fixing the size of blade to give the required area, consideration must be given to the tip speed, aspect ratio (as in the case of a wing, span divided by chord, or length divided by width) and to such factors as propulsive efficiency, noise, weight and blade rigidity. In the days of piston engines most blades had an aspect ratio much higher than most wings and a small rounded tip, and it was rare to see more than three blades on one hub. Today there is far more variety. Light aircraft typically have two blades of traditional shape. Turboprops have up to six blades, in order to achieve the blade area needed to transmit the power at high altitudes whilst still rotating slowly enough for noise to be a minimum. Turboprops with modern multi-blade propellers can usually demonstrate the lowest fuel burn and lowest airfield noise level for cruising speeds up to 400 knots (say, 460 m.p.h.), but drawbacks include the weight and cost (to buy and to maintain) of the propeller and the reduction gear on the engine, and possibly higher noise and vibration levels inside the aircraft, compared with a jet.

17. Contra-Rotating Propellers

For a period towards the end of World War II, and just after, the contra-rotating propeller with two banks of blades geared to run in opposite directions offered a way of providing enough blades to absorb really high powers. There were other important advantages too; the absence of whirl in the slipstream meant that no energy was wasted in producing a rotation which had no useful reaction associated with it, and steady flow over the control surfaces was much less troublesome than one that whirled. Gyroscopic effects were cancelled out, and the division of the engine torque between two oppositely rotating propellers left no resultant torque to be passed to the airframe. Today contra-rotation is returning with the introduction of propfans.

Propfans are a species of propulsion system which bridges the gap between turbofans and turboprops. Unlike the turboprop, in which the propeller is considered a separate entity, the propulsive blades of a propfan are an integral part of the engine, and they may be enclosed in a surrounding shroud as is the fan of a turbofan. These blades (Plate 28) are exceedingly thin and swept back like scimitars in order to provide quiet and efficient propulsion at jet speeds. Single-rotation propfans offer fuel consumption 8–10 per cent lower than the best turbofans. Contra-rotating propfans offer a gain of 25–30 per cent (Plate 27). Usually the front and rear fans have different numbers of blades, such as eight on one and ten on the other. Of course, in most propfans a reduction-gear drive is needed, as in a turboprop.

18. Altitude Effects

Working conditions become worse for the propeller as the aircraft climbs; the speed of sound is less in the rarefied atmosphere and it also becomes difficult for the blades to handle a sufficient mass of the less dense air. If the blade tips are already running close to the speed of sound it is impossible to compensate for the reduced density by increasing the propeller speed; it may be possible to compensate by increasing the pitch of the blades, though this may create more turbulence. The overall effect of altitude is such that by the time an aircraft has climbed to 40,000 feet the propeller can only handle about one-quarter of the power it can absorb at sea-level.

19. Variable-Pitch and Constant-Speed Mechanisms

The mechanisms used to vary the pitch differ in detail but most rely on a mechanical governor to hold the speed within a selected range and use hydraulic pressure to alter the pitch. Some early propellers used electric motors to control blade pitch, and there are several other methods. Almost all the latest propellers used on commuter airliners also have what is called a Beta mode in which, usually on the ground, the pilot can control pitch directly. In the air, however, pitch variation is automatic.

Automatic devices are common in the control of aircraft engines because their use allows the engine to be operated at its best but without risk of overloading. The speed control for propellers offers a suitable introduction to the idea of automatic controls.

In the mechanism shown in Fig. 6 speed control is given by a pair of spring-loaded flyweights which move out as speed increases and lift the oil control valve by bearing on a collar formed on the spindle. Control valves differ in detail but all contrive to direct a supply of high-pressure oil against a piston inside the propeller hub and the piston movement is used to change the blade pitch. If the speed increases enough to bring the governor into action the blades are moved to a coarser pitch and the increased drag on the blades holds the speed within the selected limits. As soon as the speed has returned to the correct value the flyweights return to the 'on speed'

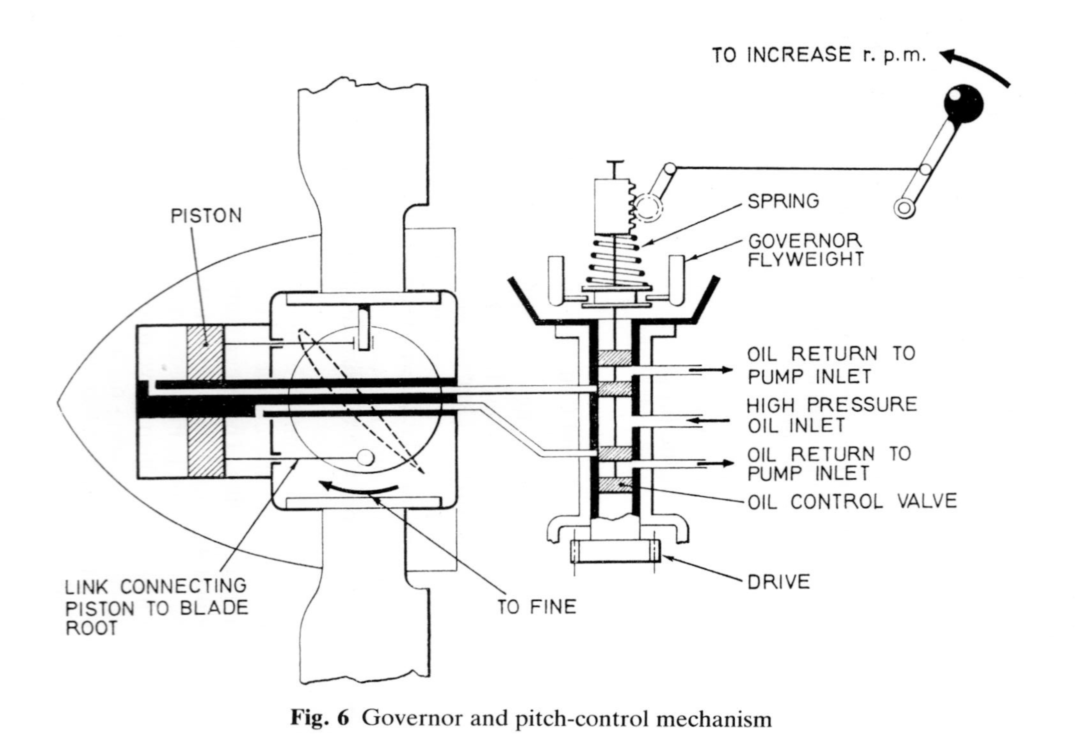

Fig. 6 Governor and pitch-control mechanism

position and set the control valve so that the piston chamber is isolated from hydraulic pressure.

The hand control used to select the particular speed required to be held constant by the governor functions by altering the load on the spring. Compression of the spring requires the flyweights to rotate at a higher speed before sufficient force can be exerted to lift the control valve and bring the pitch change mechanism into action. Releasing the load has the reverse effect and dictates a lower speed to be maintained by the system.

Fig. 6 also shows one way in which hydraulic pressure may be used to change the pitch; in this case there are links connecting the piston to each of the blade roots so as to convert the fore and aft movement of the piston into rotation of the blades.

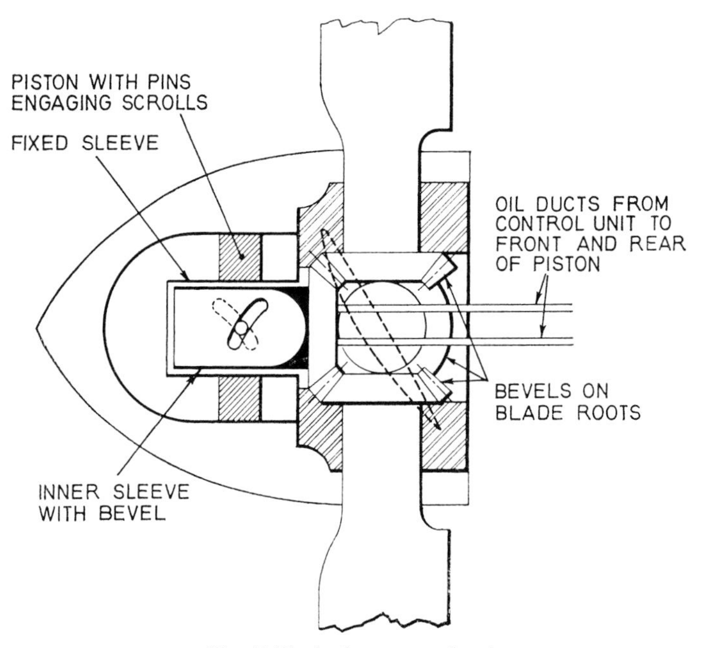

Fig. 7 Pitch-change mechanism

At first glance the mechanism shown in Fig. 7 does not look so straightforward but this is an impression brought about by the compact nature of the unit. Each blade has a bevel formed on its root which engages another bevel carried on a sleeve coaxial with the propeller shaft. This sleeve has helical slots in it and is surrounded by a fixed sleeve which is anchored to the hub; the fixed sleeve also has helical slots, but spiralling in the opposite direction to those in the bevel sleeve. Pins carried by the piston engage these slots so that as the piston moves, the inner sleeve and its bevel are forced to turn against the reaction provided by the fixed sleeve. Rotation of the inner sleeve and bevel causes the blades to rotate and give a change of pitch.

It will be realized by this time that power is required to rotate the propeller and that at really high speeds of flight extra power is swallowed up in forcing the blades round against the high resistance set up when shock waves are formed. There are two sources of power in common use: piston engines which are used exclusively for propeller drives, and turbines which may be used with propellers or for jet propulsion. Our next tasks are to study how these engines develop power and find out the application to which each is most suited.

20. The Engine Cycle

Piston engines and turbines have much in common although in appearance and in the manner of working they are not at all alike. Both are air-breathing engines, that is, atmospheric air is used to provide the oxygen needed for combustion and to provide the gases which the engineers describe as the working substance. These engines are both of the internal-combustion variety, so called because the energy that is released comes from burning a mixture of fuel and air inside the engine. In this respect they are quite different from steam engines in which the working substance – steam – is produced in boilers remote from the engine and never comes in contact with the products of combustion. The internal-combustion engine offers a much more direct way of utilizing heat energy and it is more efficient and lighter than the steam plants. The steam plants can, however, consume fuels which would not be acceptable inside an internal-combustion engine. (Gas turbines have been run quite successfully on pulverized solid fuels such as coal and peat but liquid or gaseous fuels offer such tremendous advantages from the distribution point of view that there is little incentive to install and operate the costly equipment needed for solid fuels.)

The air that is 'breathed' by aircraft engines is subject to a cycle of operations which is very similar for piston engines and turbines although the machinery used is totally different. In each case the air has to be induced (i.e. got into the engine), then it is compressed, fuel is supplied and ignited, and the burning gases are expanded to convert the heat energy to a directly useful form and then exhausted to the atmosphere. Briefly, the steps in the cycles are induction, compression, ignition, expansion, and exhaust.

21. The Importance of Compression

It is easy to see why air should be taken into the engines, why burning should take place, and why the spent gases must be exhausted to atmosphere, but why is compression an essential step in the process of power generation? When fuel is burned in an open fire the air is not compressed in advance, yet burning seems to take place all right and the fire provides the necessary warmth and comfort expected of it. Inside an engine we expect work to be done and somehow the heat must be harnessed for this task. Perhaps the easiest way to see how this is done is to consider the reverse process and think about what happens when work is done on the air, and then work backwards to get some ideas on how air or other gases can be made to do work.

In the days when bicycles were much more widely used and tyres were much less reliable, most people had some experience of using bicycle pumps and most realized that the part of the pump which is usually held in the left hand could get quite hot in the process of inflating a tyre. The physical effort put into working the pump appears to some extent in the form of heat – mechanical work is in fact converted to heat by the act of compressing the air. If the air is subsequently allowed to expand it is reasonable to expect heat to be converted to work, but because of various losses in the two processes there will be rather less energy recovered than was put into it originally. During the expansion process the compressed air may do work by pushing a piston along inside a cylinder or it may be used to impart kinetic energy as in the case of the jet engine. These two applications of the use of compressed air are sometimes demonstrated, unexpectedly perhaps, with bicycle pump and tyre; if the valve jams open the pressure in the tyre is capable of forcing the pump plunger out quite violently, or if the valve is pulled out the rush of air shows that the stored energy has been converted to kinetic energy. The amount of energy converted in either of these expansion processes depends on the pressure reached at the end of compression. Think of what happens when the valve is taken from a deflated tyre: nothing. However, if there is considerable pressure in the tyre when the valve is removed there is no mistaking that the air in the tyre has been set in motion by releasing it. You may even get the impression that the air becomes colder as it rushes out. This certainly does happen, since the store of heat energy is reduced, but whether the temperature drop is sufficient to be detected by the senses is another matter. However, perhaps we are getting round to the idea that to make the best use of the heat energy available the burning must take place at an elevated pressure so that the heat may be converted to a useful form of mechanical energy as the pressure is let down to atmospheric, or thereabouts.

In the descriptions of hardware that follow, a study will be made of how these processes are carried out so as to be both effective and efficient. This dual aspect is important in the case of aircraft engines because efficiency can sometimes be obtained at the cost of added complications and weight; a careful balance must always be made to check that the savings in cost or weight of fuel justify the steps taken to achieve them.

22. Two Strokes and Four Strokes

The cycle of operations carried out in any given piston engine may be completed in one revolution of the crankshaft or in two, according to type. As one revolution of the crankshaft causes each piston to move from one end of the cylinder to the other and back again thus completing two strokes, an engine which completes the cycle in one revolution is known as a *two-stroke* and one which requires two revolutions to complete the cycle is known as a *four-stroke*.

Many of the events that take place in an engine are described relative to the two extremes of piston travel which are referred to as *top dead centre* (t.d.c.) when the piston is at the outer end of its travel and *bottom dead centre* (b.d.c.) when it is at the inner end. These two positions are shown in Fig. 8. Because the piston position depends on the position of the crank it is not unusual to say that the piston is 'so many degrees before t.d.c.' or that 'the crank is at t.d.c.' The expressions may be slightly loose but the meanings are quite clear.

The two-stroke engine can be made in a very simple form (Fig. 9) with only three moving parts per cylinder: the crankshaft, connecting rod, and piston. Perhaps because of their extreme simplicity these engines sometimes lack refinements that could prevent irregular idling, and the fuel consumption suffers because of restrictions imposed on the timing by the port arrangement. (The ports are open for a very limited time, the transfer port and the exhaust port are open together for a little while, and the periods of opening are evenly distributed on either side of the dead-centre position.

Virtually no two-stroke engines were used for aircraft propulsion in 1924–80 apart from a handful of diesels. Today thousands of small two-strokes are used in microlights, and two-stroke diesels are also

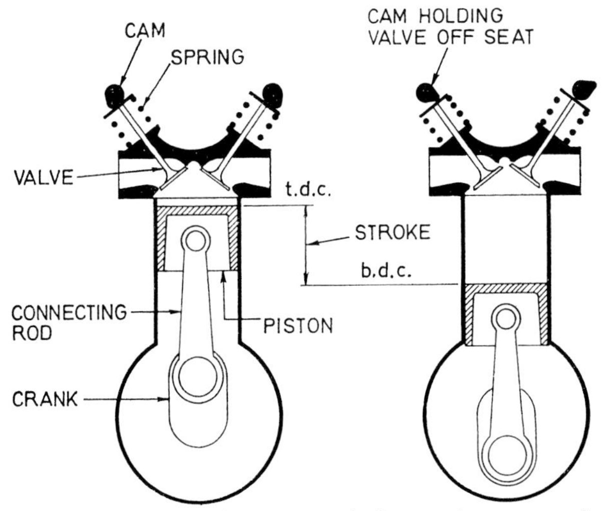

Fig. 8 Four-stroke engine with one camshaft per valve or row of valves

coming back into fashion, one new Soviet engine being in the 200 h.p. class (Plate 9). Of course, at first glance an engine clever enough to get rid of its exhaust near b.d.c. and *simultaneously* draw in a fresh charge of combustible mixture might be thought twice as powerful as an equivalent four-stroke. In practice, there are complications, notably that the exhaust and fresh mixture get mixed up so that efficiency and power suffer.

23. The Practical Four-Stroke Engine

Figure 8 shows a very simple single-cylinder engine designed to run on the four-stroke cycle. Already it is possible to detect the inevitable trend towards complication as the designers seek to improve performance, and although many parts have been left out of the diagram in the interests of clarity there are still many more than would be required, for example, in a two-stroke. Practical considerations such as provisions for adjustment and access to the mechanism for attention may dictate the layout adopted but more details of these will be given later.

The fresh charge of air and fuel enters the cylinder by a port formed in the head, and the exhaust gases leave by a similar port on the other side of the head. Gas flow through these ports is controlled by valves, which are held in the closed position by springs and opened when required by cams acting on the valve stems and overcoming the

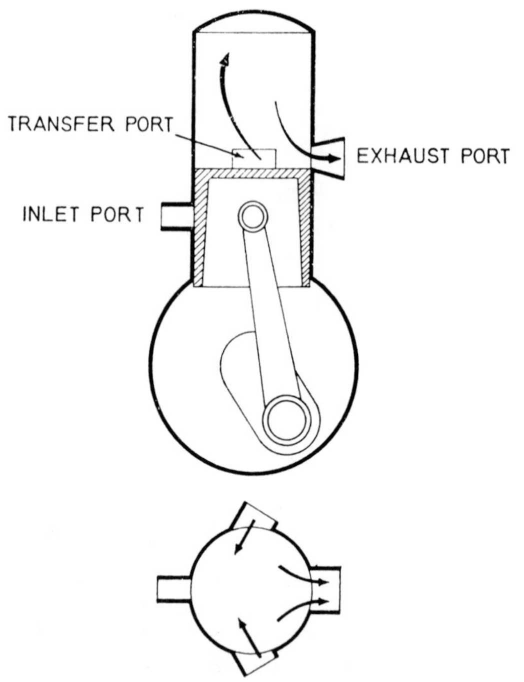

Fig. 9 Three-port two-stroke engine

spring load. Naturally the process of opening and closing the valves is not an instantaneous one as such action would give rise to prohibitively high loads. There are certain far-reaching effects involved in providing a less violent valve movement which will be considered after a preliminary look at our simple engine. Since it only exists on paper, this engine cannot suffer from the metal fatigue that could trouble a real engine with excessively rapid valve movements!

The two camshafts are geared to run at half crankshaft speed so that each valve is opened and closed once in every two revolutions and remains off its seat for about half a revolution of the crankshaft. The cycle may be considered to start with the piston at top dead centre and both valves on their seats. The inlet valve opens as the piston begins to move downwards and a mixture of fuel and air enters the cylinder. As the piston reaches b.d.c. the valve closes, and both valves remain on their seats as the piston rises and compresses the mixture. The mixture is heated by compression and by contact with the hot metal parts of the engine and prepared for combustion which is started by a carefully timed spark. Burning takes place rapidly (sometimes violently) raising the temperature and pressure inside the cylinder so that as soon as the piston passes t.d.c. it is forced along the cylinder to give the power stroke. By the time the piston has reached b.d.c. no further use can be made of the energy in the hot gases so the exhaust valve is opened and remains open for the whole of the next stroke while the piston rises and the exhaust gases are expelled. A lot of energy has to be released in this way – about one-third of the total yield from the burning process – but any device for harnessing this heat would almost certainly be too costly and too heavy to be worth while. Since the amount of heat carried away in the exhaust has just been mentioned, it is not out of place to record that another third of the heat from the fuel is taken away by the cooling system, leaving only one-third available to do useful work. Figure 10 gives a pictorial summary of the sequence known as the four-stroke cycle.

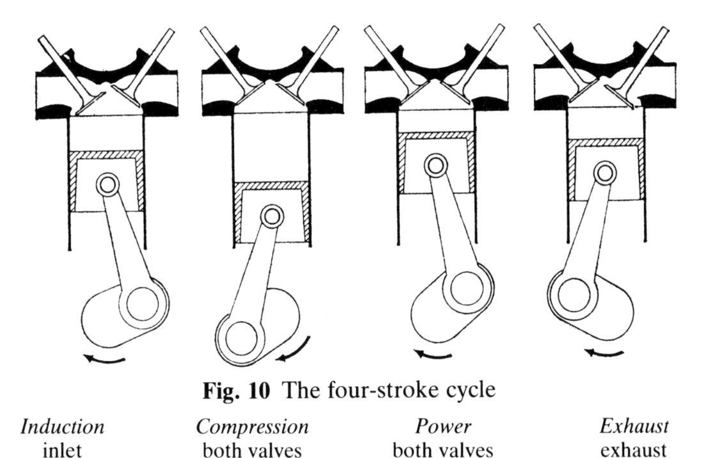

Fig. 10 The four-stroke cycle

Induction	*Compression*	*Power*	*Exhaust*
inlet valve open	both valves closed	both valves closed	exhaust valve open

It has already been suggested that it is unreasonable to expect the valves to open and close instantaneously and in fact the acceleration and retardation are spread over quite a large arc of crank movement. This less violent action is made possible by the fact that for quite a few degrees of crankshaft movement either side of the dead centre positions there is very little piston movement. During the time the crank is within what is known as the *ineffective crank angle* there is little or no change in the combustion chamber size and very little tendency for the piston to pump gases into or out of the cylinder. In these circumstances it does not matter much if the valves are not on their seats, and this situation provides a suitable opportunity for spreading the processes of opening and closing over a reasonable interval so as to prevent excessive loadings.

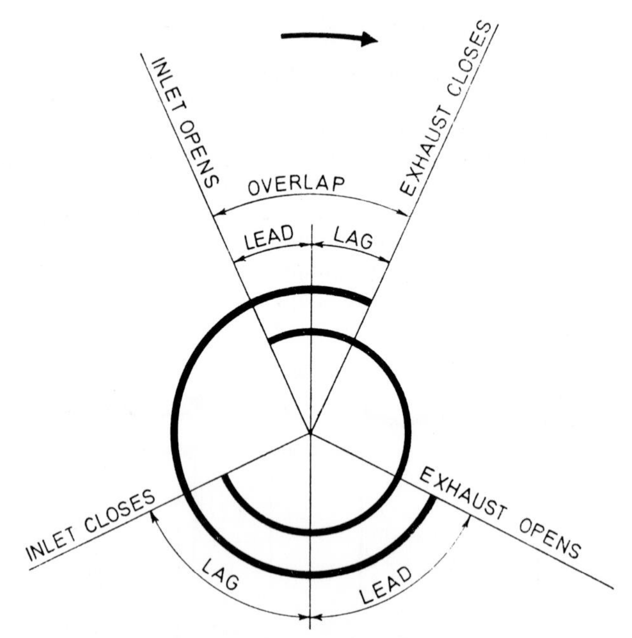

Fig. 11 Valve-timing diagram

Figure 11 is a typical timing diagram showing how soon the valves start to open before the dead centres and how long it is before they finally close after them. When a valve opens before the piston is at the dead centre position it is said to *lead*; when it closes after the piston has passed the dead centre position it is said to *lag*. During the short interval when both valves are off their seats at the same time they are said to *overlap*.

As the inlet valve is open after b.d.c. it might appear that there is a risk of blowing fresh charge back through the inlet port, but this rarely happens since the downgoing piston lowers the pressure in the cylinder and therefore the piston has to rise perceptibly on the next stroke before equalizing, let alone exceeding, the pressure in the induction system.

Although the exhaust valve appears to open very early this does not entail any serious loss of power, as the position of the crank is such that the force in the connecting rod can do very little about turning the crank. It is rather like trying to propel a bicycle by standing on the pedal when it is at the bottom of its travel.

24. Poppet-Valve Mechanism

The choice of mechanisms used to operate poppet valves is dictated by the speed at which the engine is expected to run and on how much the customer is prepared to pay. The arrangement shown in Fig. 8 with one camshaft per valve or row of valves, gives the least possible reciprocating mass and offers the possibility of running at higher speeds than some of the other systems depicted. Camshafts of this kind result in tall engines, and the drive may be costly because provision has to be made for the expansion of the cylinder block and for uncoupling the drive when access to the valves is required.

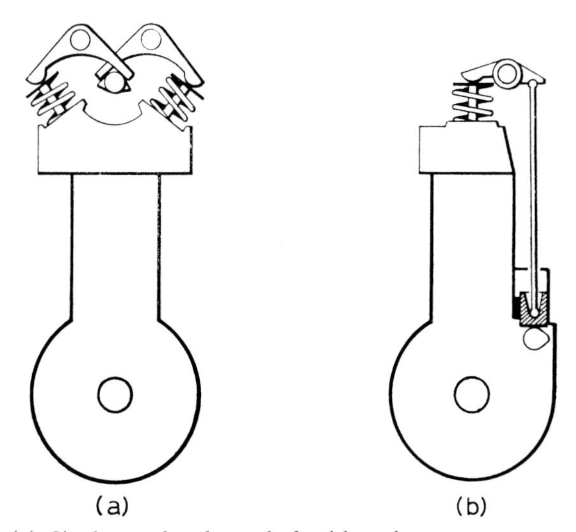

Fig. 12 (*a*) Single overhead camshaft with rockers
(*b*) Low-level camshaft with cam follower, push rod and rocker

The other two arrangements, shown in Figs. 12*a* and 12*b*, use single camshafts and for this reason are less costly, but the additional moving parts restrict speed if forces are to be kept within reasonable limits. There is not much to choose between the various poppet-valve mechanisms provided care is taken to keep the parts as light as possible without sacrificing the necessary stiffness. Figures 13 and 14

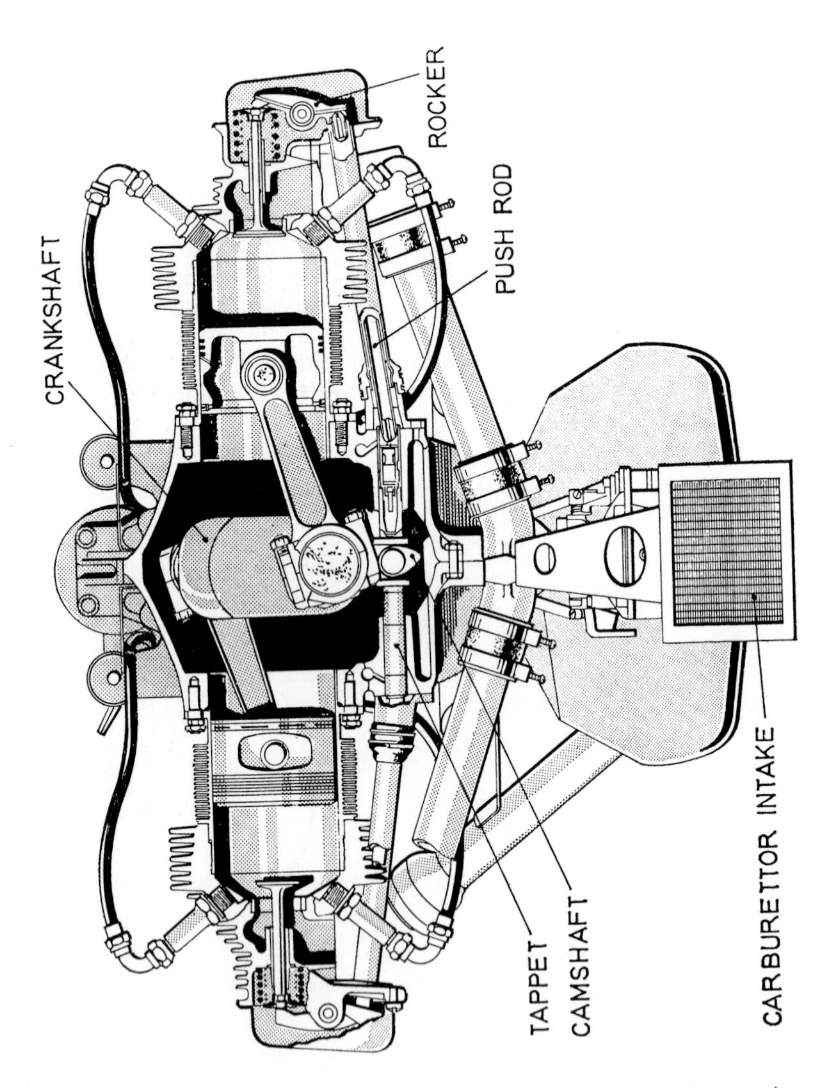

Fig. 13 Section through a pair of cylinders of a Continental flat-four engine

Shows how a single camshaft positioned under the crankshaft serves both cylinder banks through the medium of tappets, push rods and rockers

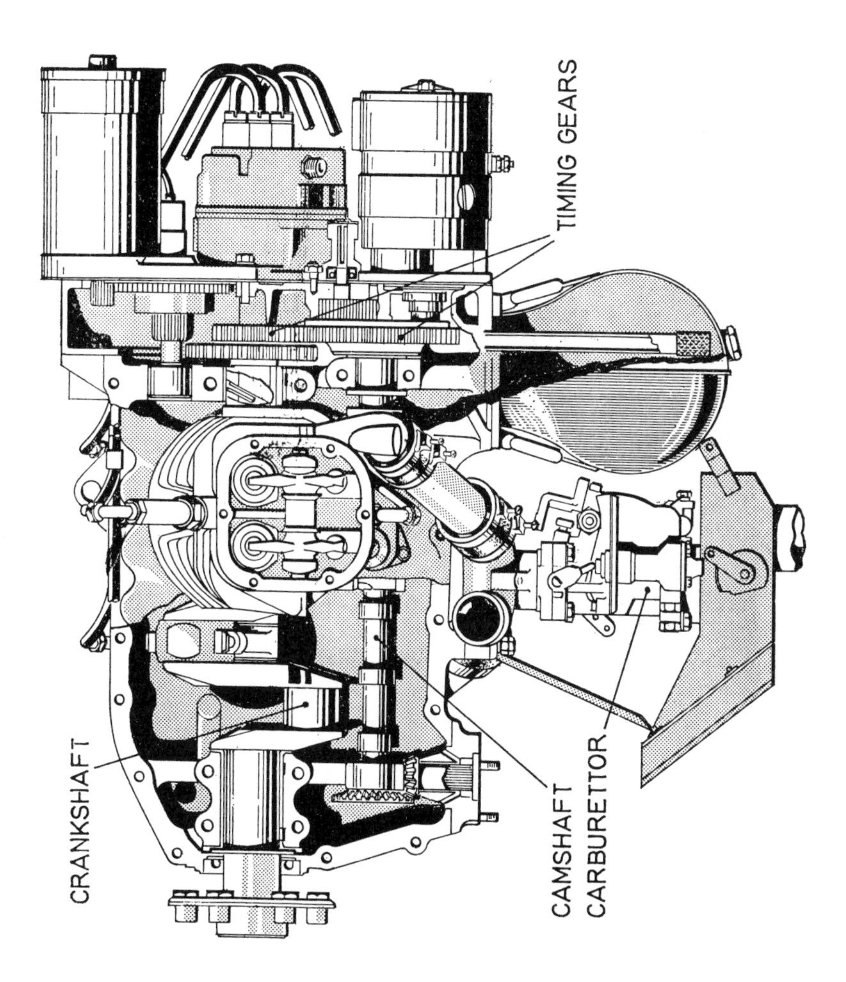

Fig. 14 Section through Continental flat-four engine

In addition to showing the simple gear drive to the camshaft this view reveals the short crankshaft that can be used when the cylinders are arranged in pairs on opposite sides of the crankshaft show the straightforward single camshaft arrangement with tappets, push rods and rockers that is used in the Continental flat-four and flat-six engines. Plate 6 gives an inverted view of part of the single camshaft used in conjunction with four valves and four rockers per cylinder – an arrangement that has been typical of Rolls-Royce practice for many years in their large aircraft engines.

25. Sleeve Valves

For many years exhaust valves were the weakest link in the chain of parts that made up the piston engine. Long exposure to hot gases and indifferent cooling arrangements caused splits and distortion that leaked away pressure from the cylinders and called for frequent servicing. The way in which hot valves are responsible for detonation and loss of power receives more attention in Section 57.

In November 1926 the Engine Department of the Bristol Aeroplane Company took up the development of a form of sleeve-valve engine which had been tried in cars and motor cycles with limited success. This type of engine uses a single sleeve, sliding between each piston and cylinder, to uncover inlet and exhaust ports formed in the cylinder walls. The sleeve is driven at half engine speed by a small crank engaging with a self-aligning bearing carried in a housing at the base of the sleeve. These components are shown in Plate 7, where it is also possible to detect the peculiar shape of the ports. This shape is dictated by the need to provide free and adequate passages whilst at the same time allowing for the fact that at one part of the cycle the sleeve ports must move between the cylinder ports without uncovering them.

Naturally the sleeve valve was not without its problems – very few engineering products are so perfect that there is no call to improve them. The piston, sleeve and cylinder start off at the same temperature when cold, but under working conditions the piston is hotter than the sleeve and that in turn is hotter than the cylinder. To maintain correct working clearances at all temperatures was impossible in the early applications of sleeve valves to motor-car engines, but a careful choice of materials with suitable expansion coefficients reduced this problem in aircraft engines. The deeply recessed sparking plug was not easy to cool and this did much to encourage the development of heat-resisting plugs!

The elimination of the hot spot caused by the hot exhaust valve cut down servicing requirements and allowed the sleeve-valve engine to run at higher pressures than the poppet-valve engine without the same risk of detonation. The smooth continuous motion of the sleeve compared with the jerky action of poppet-valve mechanisms has always attracted engineers as has the positive opening and closing of ports.

When piston engines were in their heyday opinion was about equally divided over the relative merits of sleeve valves and poppet valves. Competition was keen and healthy, forcing the solution of problems that might otherwise have been allowed to persist. The sodium-cooled exhaust valve is a case in point. These valves have hollow stems containing sodium which becomes molten at the engine working temperatures. As the molten sodium is thrown about inside the valve, heat is carried from the head to the stem and hence to the guide and the coolant much more rapidly than is the case with a solid valve relying on conduction to get rid of the heat. Perhaps opinion finally came down in favour of the sleeve valve, as the mighty Rolls-Royce Eagle of World War II was a sleeve-valve engine with 24 cylinders arranged in four banks with six cylinders in each. However, the emergence of the lighter and more powerful gas turbine at about the same time kept the Eagle from the production line.

26. Inertia of Moving Parts

Some stress has already been laid on the forces involved in moving and reciprocating parts of the valve gear, and rightly so, as these parts can be a source of noise and give rise to the need for adjustment if allowance is not made for the exacting working conditions. The pistons also experience *inertia*, that is they have a natural reluctance to move if already at rest or to stop if already in motion.

Although the crankshaft may be turning at a perfectly steady rate, the pistons have to be brought to rest and accelerated again twice per revolution. In quite an ordinary engine this can easily involve the pistons in 5,000 reversals per minute and there may be 12,000 or more in a high-performance engine; the turn-round is a hurried process involving heavy forces. Every time the piston reaches t.d.c. it tends to heave the engine up and when it reaches b.d.c. the opposite is true. Such repeated applications of force must tend to cause vibration and everything possible is done to minimize the effects felt outside the engine. A sizeable and very interesting book could be written on this subject of engine vibration, especially if we dared to use formulae and get down to details. However, it is possible to understand something of the problem without having to wrestle with the calculus.

The magnitude of the forces acting on the piston depends on the weight of the piston, how far it has to move during each stroke, and rotating. A statement of the obvious perhaps but it does let us think about the things that might be done to keep the forces within bounds, like reducing the stroke for example. If this is done piston diameter has to be increased to retain the same swept volume, so there is a little more weight with which to contend. Fortunately the weight increase is not enough to offset the benefits that come from using a shorter stroke and running the engine faster for the same inertia forces. This packs in more power strokes per minute, which means more power.

A comparison between the large piston engines in use at the end of World War II and their smaller counterparts of the present time illustrates a change in ideas that has taken place concerning the proportions of bore and stroke. In the engines of World War II the stroke was greater than the bore, sometimes very much so, and earned for this type of engine the description *long stroke*. Light aircraft engines of the present time have bores which are very much larger than the stroke and go by the mysterious title of *oversquare*. This title has grown from the practice of calling engines *square* if the bore is equal to the stroke. The two engines shown in Fig. 15 have

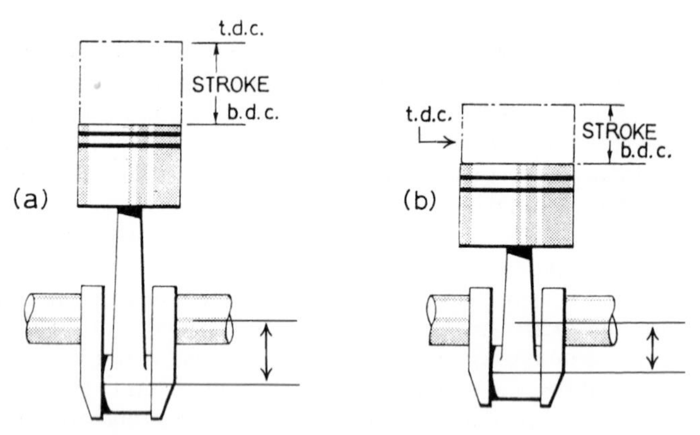

Fig. 15 (*a*) Long-stroke engine (*b*) Oversquare engine

Each engine has the same swept volume and the same ratio of connecting-rod length to crank throw

equal swept volumes, that is they swallow equal volumes of mixture at each induction stroke, but the ratios of stroke to bore are different. The long-stroke engine is seen to be taller and the oversquare engine might be longer because of the extra space taken up by the bigger bores. In addition to the advantage of being able to run faster without exceeding safe inertia loads, the oversquare engine has more room for valves of adequate size with space for cooling round the seats.

It takes a lot of juggling with possible values of bore, stroke and r.p.m. to decide what combination is going to give the most attractive engine. Once the dimensions are fixed the materials will have to be specified. The choice of a light alloy for the piston seems obvious enough, but sometimes restrictions on space require the use of high-strength steel. On the other hand the light alloy scores as an aid to cooling because of its ability to conduct heat away from the piston crown and transfer it to the skirt and hence to the cylinder and the cooling system. Heat transfer in this way is so important that it is not uncommon to use thicker sections than are needed for strength so as to ensure an adequate path for the heat.

27. Balancing the Reciprocating Parts

Any piston controlled by a conventional connecting rod reaches its maximum speed when the crank and connecting rod are at right-angles to one another, and this happens well before the crank has turned through 90 degrees from t.d.c. In consequence, the down-going piston accelerates to maximum speed in less than 90 degrees of crank movement, and spreads the retardation over more than 90 degrees as the piston moves towards b.d.c. On the return journey from b.d.c., the crank turns through more than 90 degrees to bring the piston up to maximum speed and then retards it in less than 90 degrees. When the piston is going to and from t.d.c. the forces involved are greater than when going to and from b.d.c.

There is no practical way of obtaining complete balance in a single-cylinder engine. It can only be obtained by adding such complications that the engine becomes more of an exercise in ingenuity than anything else, and since single-cylinder engines are only attractive because they are simple, no one is likely to give this up for better balance. The first step towards achieving better balance is to add another cylinder and make the extra complication work for its living. If the pistons are to give a measure of balance they must be linked to cranks spaced at 180 degrees to one another, and the cylinders may be side by side as in Fig. 16*a* or horizontally opposed as in Fig. 16*b*. Of these arrangements the latter is slightly better because the forces set up by each piston exactly balance one another leaving only a couple tending to pivot the engine to and fro about a vertical axis. With the cylinders side by side the forces do not balance out entirely and there is a couple tending to rock the engine about a horizontal

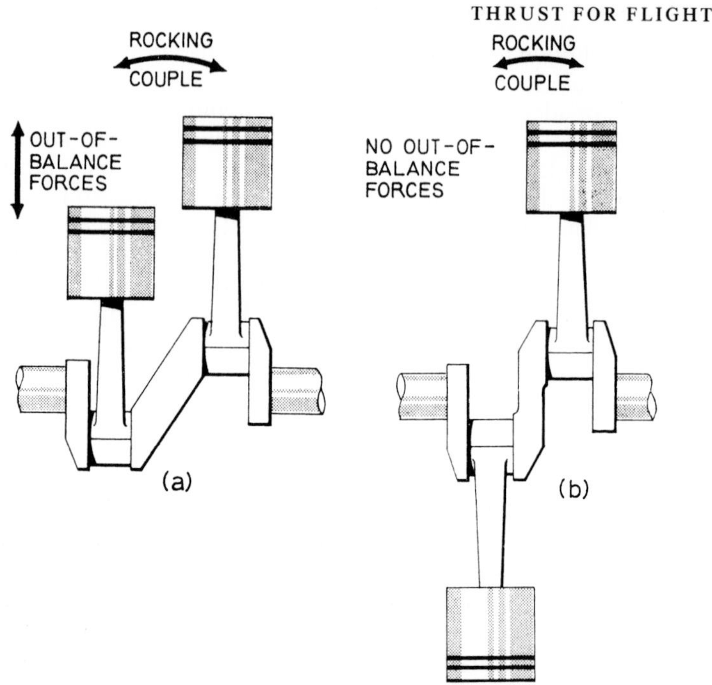

Fig. 16 (*a*) Cylinders side by side
(*b*) Cylinders horizontally opposed

axis. The out-of-balance force is less with long connecting rods than with short ones, because the longer the rod, the nearer the piston comes to accelerating in 90 degrees and retarding in 90 degrees.

Fig. 17 shows graphically the forces needed to accelerate and retard a typical piston as the crank turns through one revolution. In this case the force set up by the piston is zero at 75 degrees and again at 285 degrees because these are the crank positions at which this particular piston is at maximum speed – it is on the point of changing over from acceleration to retardation. The angles at which the speed is greatest depend on the ratio of connecting rod length to crank throw and vary between one design and another; a long connecting rod is best but it does add to the height of the engine. The decision-makers have plenty to think about before making the final choice.

The odd effect of these unequal accelerations is shown by adding to the diagram the forces set up by another piston which goes up as the other goes down, that is, the cranks driving the pistons are at 180 degrees to each other. If due attention is paid to the sense or direc-

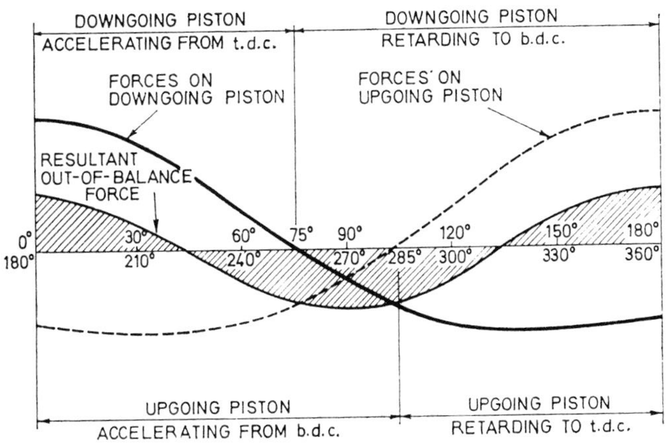

Fig. 17 Inertia forces

tion of the forces it will be seen that during part of the revolution the forces oppose one another and during two intervals of about 30 degrees each they act together. The resultant forces applied to the engine structure act upwards at t.d.c. and at b.d.c. and downwards at the mid position of piston travel – a state of affairs that would never have been expected if some simple arithmetic had not been done to check on the forces. When the forces are in opposition, out-of-balance couples are set up and tend to rock the engine about an axis at right-angles to the plane containing the crankshaft and cylinders. The extent to which these out-of-balance forces and couples make themselves felt depends on many things, such as the weight of the engine (as this determines the capacity to absorb the blows), how the engine is carried in the aircraft structure, and the natural frequency with which the structure tends to vibrate. If this frequency happens to coincide with that of the out-of-balance forces the effect may only be unpleasant or it may be bad enough to fatigue some part set vibrating in harmony.

A minimum of four cylinders is generally regarded as the least number to give reasonable firing intervals. If the cylinders are in line with one another as in a normal car engine, out-of-balance forces still exist but there are no couples. In the flat-four engine (Plate 8) the forces balance out as the engine is virtually two flat twins, but there is an unbalanced couple because the pair of pistons moving to t.d.c. sets up a bigger couple than the two which are moving to b.d.c.

Apart from considerations of balance the flat four is an attractive layout for light-aircraft engines because it may use a shorter crankshaft than the in-line engine, with fewer torsional vibration problems. As noted in Section 85, engines can be cooled by air flowing past the outside of the cylinders or by liquid being pumped round internal passages. With air cooling care must be taken to ensure that cool air reaches all the hottest parts of all cylinders.

Six-cylinder engines have perfect balance provided that the crank-pins are spaced so that numbers 1 and 5 are in the same plane, numbers 2 and 5 in another at 120 degrees to this, and 3 and 4 in a third plane at 120 degrees to the other two pairs. Very small numbers of such engines are still made in Czechoslovakia.

28. Torsional Oscillations

No introduction to the problem of the vibrations that afflict the piston engine would be complete without some reference to the torsional oscillations that may occur in the crankshafts. When a shaft has to transmit a torque or twisting moment it must wind up to some extent and spring back again when released. If the shaft must have a lot of kinks in it to provide cranks, the twisting moments are hard to resist and perceptible deflection may take place. A steady twisting moment may have few ill effects, but the repeated applications of force to which a crankshaft is subjected may set up oscillations as the shaft recovers the original shape between impulses. At certain speeds the impulses may coincide with the natural vibration period of the shaft and give very rough running even in an engine which is in good mechanical balance. Shafts must be as short as possible, adequately supported and counterweighted to minimize these torsional effects.

The two-throw crankshaft for a radial engine, as shown in Plates 13 and 14, is short and might therefore be expected to have reasonable freedom from torsional oscillations, but the components used in the counterweight system (Plate 14) indicate the steps that have had to be taken to provide damping. The problem of forces in radial engines is a complex one compared with that of engines in which the cylinders are parallel. For one thing, simple addition and subtraction of forces cannot be applied as was done in Fig. 17; instead there would have to be vectorial addition (or the equivalent mathematical solutions) to an extent that is not justified here. The even spacing of the cylinders may give a false impression that with symmetry all will be well, but a look at one difference only should be enough to put us on our guard. Although the crankpin end of the master connecting rod (Plate 15) follows a circular path, the corresponding ends of the other rods do not and the motion of the other pistons and the forces on them differ. The vibrations may or may not be aggravated by the manner in which successive power impulses are applied. The firing order is 1, 3, 5, 2, 4, for a five-cylinder engine as shown in Fig. 18, that is, every second cylinder fires in turn so that the impulses are applied at equal intervals to the crankshaft. If you think this matter over carefully you will probably see why the radial engine has an odd number of cylinders in each row.

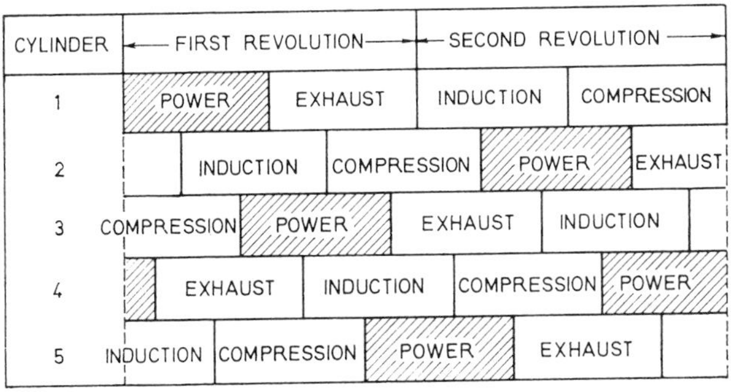

CYLINDER	← FIRST REVOLUTION →		← SECOND REVOLUTION →	
1	POWER	EXHAUST	INDUCTION	COMPRESSION
2	INDUCTION	COMPRESSION	POWER	EXHAUST
3	COMPRESSION	POWER	EXHAUST	INDUCTION
4	EXHAUST	INDUCTION	COMPRESSION	POWER
5	INDUCTION	COMPRESSION	POWER	EXHAUST

Fig. 18 Firing sequence of five-cylinder radial engine

29. Turbojets

During World War II thousands of high-power piston engines were built every month, all extremely complicated and heavy. By contrast the newly invented turbojet seemed a model of unbelievable simplicity and light weight, though Lord Hives, the farsighted head of Rolls-Royce, predicted 'Don't worry, we'll soon design the simplicity out of it!'.

How right he was, but we can begin with the simplest and most primitive form of turbojet as shown in Fig. 19. Such an engine contains a single rotating assembly consisting of a white-hot turbine at one end driving a cool compressor at the other. This is the type of engine invented by Whittle in 1929, and run in April 1937. Compared with piston engines it offered almost limitless power, simplicity, reliability, unrestricted flight speed, the ability to burn almost any liquid fuel, and many other advantages.

The simple engine shown in Fig. 19 and used for jet propulsion is known generally as a turbojet. The air is first of all compressed in a centrifugal compressor which raises the pressure to about 3½ times that at the intake (in a modern centrifugal compressor perhaps 9 times); the air then passes to the combustion chambers where fuel is added and the mixture of fuel and air ignited. Combustion takes

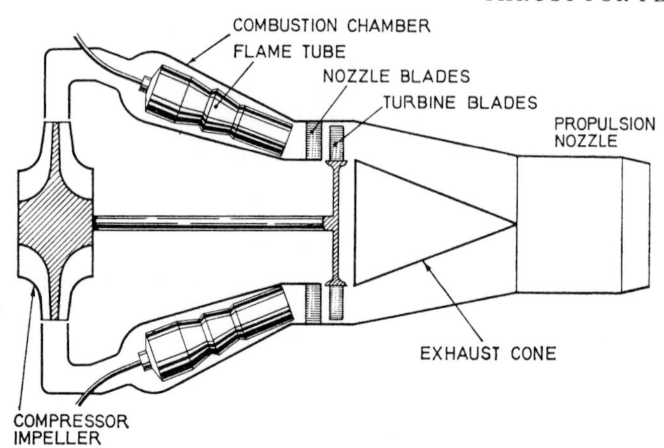

Fig. 19 Simple jet engine with single stage turbine driving double sided centrifugal compressor

place in chambers which are open at each end, so there is no rise in pressure above that of the compressor delivery. Instead, the expansion of the combustion products gives a very large increase in velocity to the gases as they pass through the nozzles, the turbine, and out at the end of the jet pipe. In the simple turbojet enough energy is extracted at the turbine to drive the compressor, and the rest of the energy is available for the expansion which gives the high velocity increase and hence the thrust. Thrust depends on how much air the engine can swallow and on the increase in velocity given to this air. The mass of air needed for combustion is not in itself sufficient to give much thrust unless the air is given a colossal and uneconomic increase in velocity. By consuming at least four times the air needed for complete combustion the thrust is obtained with a much more moderate velocity and the temperature at the turbine is reduced compared with that in the combustion zone. Without this expedient of diluting the burning gases with excess air the turbine blades would be exposed to temperatures so high that metal failure would be inevitable.

The simple turbojet just described and its descendants such as the one illustrated in Plate 16 pioneered the way for flight without propellers. As a power unit with only one major moving component, it was hailed as a masterpiece of simplification. High thrust was obtained from engines of very low weight, but the cost in fuel was heavy and the temptation was great to improve matters by adding complications and increasing the weight. Some of the variants are introduced very briefly in the next three sections but a more detailed study will have to wait until some of the limitations of the basic engines are understood.

30. Turboprops – An Introduction

In this variant of the gas turbine much more of the gas energy is extracted for shaft drive and less is made available to give jet propulsion. The propeller handles more air than the engine alone could swallow and gives greater propulsive efficiency in engines required to fly within the medium speed range. Compared with the largest piston engines, turbines are more powerful and usually lighter, so that when used in conjunction with propellers they are more economical than turbojets for speeds below 450 m.p.h. or so. The Rolls-Royce Dart engine (Plate 17) is a good example of a turboprop which has been produced in very large numbers and has bridged the gap between the large piston engines and the turbojet.

31. Turbofans, Ducted Fans and By-pass Engines – An Introduction

In these engines the propeller is replaced by a multi-bladed fan or fans, running inside the engine casing or in a duct provided for the purpose. Various arrangements exist; in some the fan is quite distinct from the other parts of the engine whilst in others it forms part of the compressor.

32. The Gas-Turbine Cycle

In some respects the cycle of the gas turbine is similar to that of the piston engine; both take in a charge of air, compress it and burn fuel in it before expanding the products of combustion to convert the heat to mechanical energy. The efficiency with which the energy provided by the fuel is converted to the mechanical energy required depends, in both cycles, on the step-up in pressure applied to the air before combustion. It is very much easier to raise the pressure substantially in a piston-engine cylinder where the air is trapped in an enclosed space than in the rotary compressors which are virtually open at both ends. Thus, whereas piston engines fairly readily can have compression ratios exceeding 9 (or even 17 in the case of a diesel) early gas turbines often had a pressure ratio of only about 4. Over the past 40 years the technology of compressors has been transformed. Today a simple centrifugal compressor can run at a pressure ratio of 10, while axial engines can generate amazing pressure ratios exceeding 40. At supersonic speeds compression in the inlet system can multiply the overall pressure ratio dramatically.

The intermittent power impulses of the piston engine give it the benefit of a cool fresh charge in the cylinder as soon as the exhaust gases are expelled. This means that the internal parts of the combustion chamber are not exposed continuously to the extreme heat of the flame; in fact the period of exposure to maximum temperature is very short as combustion may be completed soon after the piston leaves t.d.c. Even with this very short exposure, one of the major cooling problems in the piston engine is the removal of heat from the exhaust valve heads and from the piston crowns. Conditions in the turbine are much more exacting because burning goes on continuously with no let-up for cooling. Fortunately the vast excess of air which is swallowed to improve propulsive efficiency also protects the metal from direct contact with the burning gases.

With the foregoing ideas in mind it may now be possible to make a more detailed study of the problems involved in compression, combustion and expansion in the two engine types.

33. The Compression Process

Mention has already been made in Section 21 of the need to compress the air or the air/fuel mixture so that the subsequent expansion may be effective in the conversion of heat to mechanical work. If the compression process is efficient then it should be possible to recover the energy expended in the compressor when the air is subsequently expanded, just as one expects a compressed spring to give up energy when released. If the spring is of the leaf variety used in many motor-car suspensions and there is rust between the leaves, any energy used in overcoming the friction between the leaves will not be recovered. Similarly during compression of air, losses may be accounted for by mechanical friction between the piston rings and the cylinder, heat transfer between the mixture and its surroundings, and most of all by the creation of turbulence. If the gas is made to eddy, the energy used in this way can never be recovered to push the piston on its way along the expansion stroke. Some turbulence during compression may be advantageous as a means of obtaining good mixing and breaking up the flame front to speed combustion, as this reduces the risk of detonation. The need to avoid detonation limits how much compression may be used in the piston engine and will be explained further in the section dealing with fuels.

34. Compression Ratios and Pressure Ratios

The degree of compression given in the piston engine is referred to as the *compression ratio*, which in simple terms is the volume in the cylinder with the piston at b.d.c. divided by the volume at t.d.c. Fig. 8 shows the two volumes involved; if the compression ratio is quoted as 10 to 1, for example, this means that the original volume is reduced to one-tenth during compression. High compression ratios are easy enough to obtain provided care is taken to allow adequate clearance between the piston crown and the valves, which may be off their seats a little way as the exhaust stroke finishes and the induction stroke begins.

This definition of compression ratio is perfectly clear when used in connection with piston engines as being a ratio of two volumes, but unfortunately the same expression is sometimes used in gas turbine terminology for a ratio of two pressures. For anyone dealing with one engine type only, the different meanings of compression ratio are perhaps not important, but when comparisons are made between two engines as different as the turbine and the piston engine care must be taken to make the meaning clear. The difficulty arises because the pressure brought about by reducing the volume is not in simple proportion to the change in volume.

A single example should be enough to show how misleading a comparison might be if based on a misinterpretation of the definition. A compression ratio of 10 to 1 raises the pressure in a piston engine cylinder to 25 times the original value, whereas a turbine claimed to have a 'compression ratio' of 10 to 1 would only raise the pressure to 10 times the original value.

Throughout this book the expression *compression ratio* will be used only in connection with the ratio of volumes shown in Fig. 8, and the term *pressure ratio* will mean just what it says and will be applied to the rotary compressors of the turbine.

35. The Effect of Altitude on Engine Power

An adequate compression ratio is needed to ensure high efficiency, but efficiency is not the only criterion as the engine must also be capable of doing a useful job. In an aircraft the maintenance of power is of vital importance, and depends on the engine being able to swallow an adequate weight of air per minute. This becomes increasingly difficult to do as the aircraft climbs to altitudes where the air is less dense. The extent of the power loss in a piston engine can be judged from the fact that for every hundred horse-power available at sea-level there are only ten at a height of 50,000 feet. Clearly, some form of pump is needed to make the engine swallow greater volumes of air at high altitudes to compensate for the reduced density. Since there is so much loss of power, why are aircraft flown at these dizzy heights? It is, of course, attractive to fly above the weather, and people on the ground appreciate having the source of noise taken as far from them as possible, but the real reason for flying high is to achieve economy. The reduced air density results in less drag on the aircraft, and this should give a reduction in fuel consumption if sufficient power can be made available without undue penalties in the form of increased weight or reduced efficiency. In the next three sections descriptions are given of centrifugal superchargers, which have proved to be the most suitable form of pump for making the engine swallow more air at high altitudes.

36. The Centrifugal Supercharger

Over the years centrifugal compressors like the one shown in Fig. 20 have proved their suitability for use in aircraft. As the impeller runs

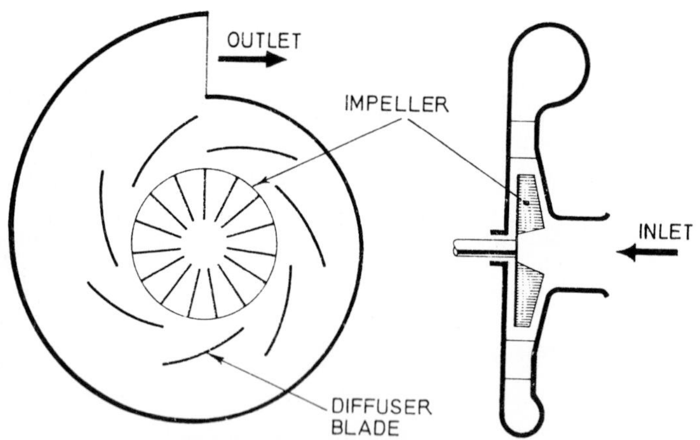

Fig. 20 Centrifugal supercharger

at very high speed the supercharger is compact considering the work it does, and the shape is suitable for mounting behind the piston engine without any increase in frontal area. There are no rubbing surfaces that need to be oiled so there is little risk of contaminating the air; the objection to contaminating the air is that too much oil in the combustion chamber leads to carbon formation and may increase the risk of detonation.

Looked upon as a machine the supercharger is a simple enough affair with only one moving part, the impeller. This is a disc with radial vanes, and a casing with stationary vanes forming *diffuser* passages surrounded by a volute or collecting chamber. The impeller imparts kinetic energy to the air which then enters the diffuser channels at a comparatively high speed. As the air passes through the divergent passages of the diffuser the speed drops and so does the kinetic energy. The total energy of the air cannot change and therefore since the kinetic energy has been reduced one of the other forms of energy must have been increased: in this case it is shown as a rise in pressure. It is an essential part of efficient energy conversion that no turbulence should be set up, as this would mean that the kinetic energy of smooth flow had merely been exchanged for the kinetic energy of turbulent flow with no rise in pressure. The impeller channels themselves provide a certain amount of diffusion and it is usual for about half the total pressure rise to take place in the impeller and half in the diffuser passages and collector ring. The rise in temperature that takes place as a result of compression is not particularly welcome as it may contribute to detonation later in the cycle. Moreover, any rise in charge temperature reduces its density, and the power of a piston engine is proportional to the mass of mixture consumed in unit time. In its passage through the supercharger the air has to accept some violent changes in speed and direction which can result in serious losses if the detail design work is not right. These losses assume more importance when this type of compressor is used in gas turbines and for this reason will receive more attention later.

The low-speed displacement type of supercharger used on marine and vehicle engines may be driven by an arrangement of V-belts which gives simplicity and flexibility, but the less bulky aircraft superchargers must be run at very high speed and require step-up gears to give the necessary ratio. Because of the inertia of the impeller, which is reluctant to change speed, the drive must incorporate some form of slipping clutch to protect the gears from overloading during speed changes. A springy element is also included in the drive to give protection from the cyclic fluctuations that occur in the rotation of piston-engine crankshafts. The successive impulses that are a feature of the piston engine might cause chatter and fatigue in the gears if these were not protected in any way.

37. Exhaust Turbines

For some applications an attractive alternative to mechanical drive is provided by using the energy in the exhaust gases to drive a turbine which is connected to the compressor as shown in Fig. 21. The turbine is almost sure to set up back pressure in the exhaust system as some price has to be paid for driving the supercharger, and it is only a question of whether this should be done at the crankshaft through a mechanical drive or through gas pressure in the cylinders. A well designed turbine can use part of the kinetic energy that is lost in the exhaust of some installations. In other installations suitable exhaust stubs may use this energy to assist with the thrust as jet propulsion; such exhaust stubs may contribute the equivalent of an eighth of the horse-power required at 375 m.p.h.

Very few aircraft engines rely on exhaust-driven superchargers alone because response to throttle changes could be sluggish, and in the event of engine stoppage at altitude a restart might be impossible because the supercharger would not rotate when the engine was motored and there might not be enough pressure at the end of the compression stroke to prepare the charge for burning.

Almost all high-power (World War II) turbosuperchargers delivered the compressed air or mixture to a second supercharger inside the engine, driven in the usual way by step-up gears from the crankshaft. The term turbosupercharger, or turbo for short, is applied to all superchargers driven by the exhaust gas. In every case the turbo is controlled by a valve called a waste gate, downstream of the turbine. This can be adjusted by the pilot, or by an automatic closed-loop control system, to maintain the optimum engine boost pressure with minimum back-pressure on the exhaust. Today's light aircraft are often fitted with turbos, but in this case there is seldom a second supercharger driven by the crankshaft (Plate 4).

38. Two-Stage Superchargers

During World War II some high-altitude engines were fitted with a two-stage mechanically driven supercharger. Figure 22 shows a two-stage supercharger which has two impellers mounted on a common shaft. The discharge from the first stage may be led directly to the eye of the second impeller or it may be passed through a cooler before going to the second stage. A cooler may also be required between the second stage and the manifold to lower the temperature before compression in the cylinder takes place. The work done during compression depends on the temperature at which compression starts, so it pays to have the air as cool as possible at the start of the process. To reach the final compressed state the air has to go through three stages of compression, two in the supercharger and one in the cylinder, but expansion takes place only over the cylinder

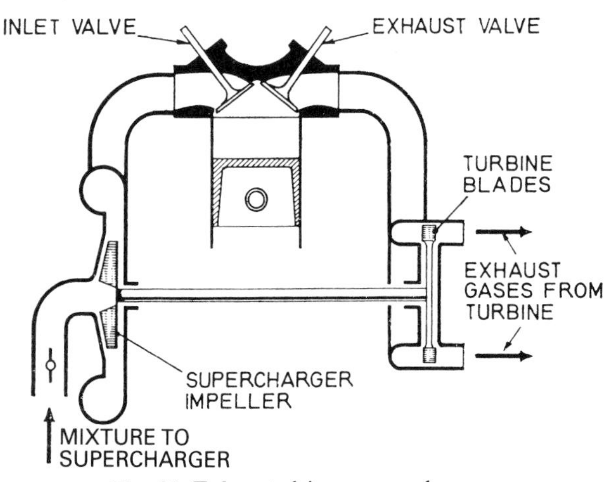

Fig. 21 Exhaust-driven supercharger

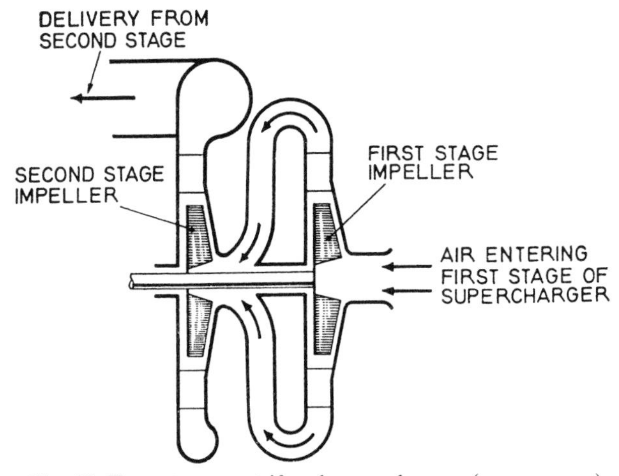

Fig. 22 Two-stage centrifugal supercharger (compressor)

stage. From the point of view of efficient conversion of heat to mechanical energy this is the stage that matters, a fact that should be remembered when remarks are made about the increase in efficiency that stems from increased compression ratio. Two-stage superchargers dramatically increase power at high altitudes, but low down they might even reduce power because of the need to close the throttle to avoid over-boosting.

39. Compression in the Gas Turbine

There are only two types of compressor currently used in aircraft turbines – the centrifugal compressor and the axial compressor. Both work on the same general principle of giving kinetic energy to the air in a high-speed rotor and converting this energy to pressure, and heat, in a set of widening passages. Each of these compressors will be dealt with later but a preliminary study of a very simple-looking compressor should help to establish some important principles.

40. Compression by Ram

Figure 23 shows a forward-facing duct mounted on an aircraft in such a position that the air entering it is free from any turbulence that

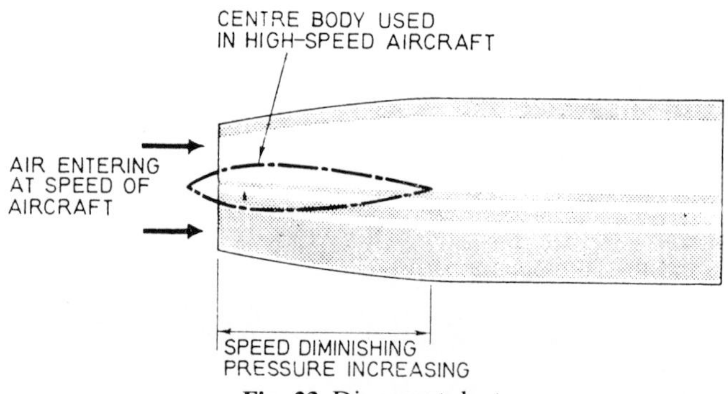

Fig. 23 Divergent duct

might be set up by adjacent parts such as the fuselage or wings. The air entering the duct has kinetic energy because of its motion relative to the aircraft, and at subsonic speeds the widening of the duct just inside the intake reduces the speed of the air with the result that the pressure rises. To get a pressure rise the widening of the duct must be gradual or turbulence might be set up and the kinetic energy frittered away in the formation of eddies.

Figure 23 shows a centrebody (it is often written as a single word) in the centre of the inlet. This is unimportant at subsonic speeds, but at supersonic speeds a movable centrebody is one of several methods of changing the area and profile of the inlet to adapt it to tremendous changes in flow.

41. Compressor Intake Losses

Usually one team designs engines while engineers in a different company design the aircraft. There has often been severe trouble because the aircraft designers failed to create an inlet system that matched the engine, and this has been especially serious with high-compression engines which were themselves designed too near the stall line and which were then installed in fighters where in combat the inlet could receive violently disturbed airflow. In any case, even in straight and level flight everything possible must be done to minimize losses in the inlet. This is important even in the relatively uncritical case of a simple centrifugal compressor.

At the entrance to the impeller the air has a relative velocity which is made up of the inflow velocity of the air and the speed of the blades which, of course, increases with the radius. As shown in Fig. 24 this

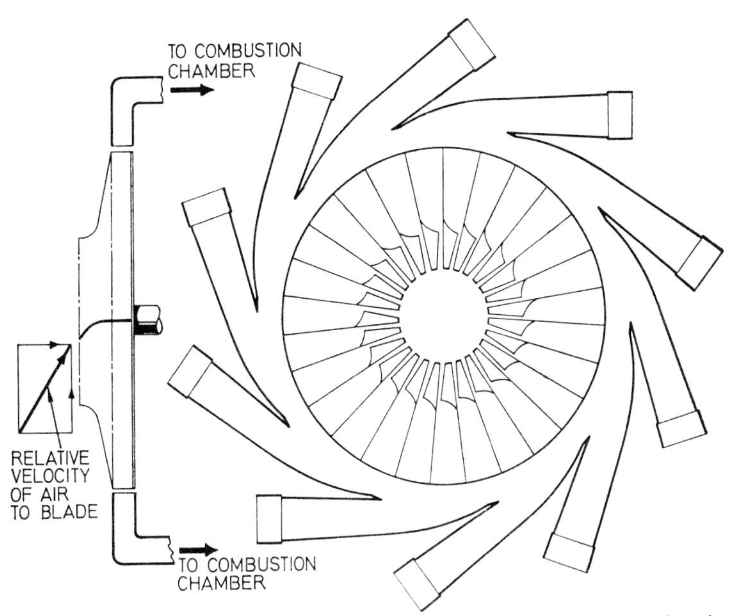

Fig. 24 Centrifugal compressor with delivery branches for ten combustion chambers

relative velocity is inclined very considerably to the compressor axis, and it is necessary to curve the blades to meet the airflow edge-on and turn the air as smoothly as possible into the radial channels. Without this curvature of the blades the air would be given considerable turbulence and this could disturb conditions right through the compressor. Any heating associated with the formation of eddies at this point has far-reaching effects: it represents a certain amount of energy used for the wrong purpose, it results in high temperatures at the compressor outlet, and as a result it restricts the amount of fuel that may be burned without exceeding the permissible maximum temperature at the turbine blades. The relative velocity at the entrance to the impeller is sufficiently high to involve the risk of shock-wave formation when working close to the limits of the compressor performance.

42. Surging

When the air leaves the impeller it has a resultant velocity that depends on how fast it travelled outwards between the blades and on how much whirl it was given before it left (Fig. 25). It is obviously

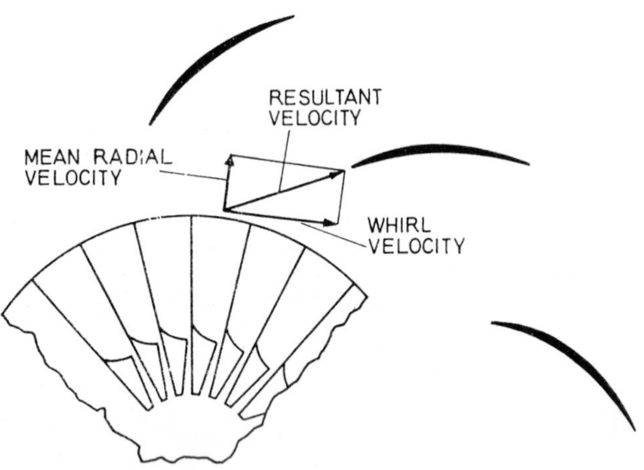

Fig. 25 Air velocity at impeller tip

desirable for the diffuser blades to be positioned so as to receive the relative airflow smoothly, but since the direction of flow changes whenever there is a change in compressor speed or in the mass flow the angle of the diffuser blades can only be a compromise. Normal practice is to use fixed diffuser blades set so as to give good results under certain chosen conditions. At other conditions of speed or airflow the air may well meet the blades at such angles of attack that turbulence occurs. All channels are not affected in the same way at the same time because the radial velocity within each impeller channel varies from a maximum in the low-pressure zone just behind the blades to a minimum in the high-pressure zone just in front of the blades. Because of this the resultant velocity across each rotor channel keeps changing. Indeed, it changes to such an extent that the angle of attack at each diffuser blade may change from positive to negative several times per revolution. As the number of impeller blades is usually more than the number of diffuser blades conditions will not be the same at every diffuser leading edge at any one moment. This results in some of the diffuser channels having smooth flow whilst others have turbulent conditions, with a rhythmic change from smooth to turbulent flow as the resultant velocity changes in each channel.

Pressure in the turbulent channels is less than in the smoothly flowing channels, because the kinetic energy changes to eddy energy instead of to pressure as it does in the channels with smooth flow. As a result of this, air may turn back over the diffuser blade tips and flow from the smooth channels to the turbulent ones. Flow in each channel alternates from smooth to turbulent and back again. This disturbed state in which the energy supplied to the compressor is simply wasted in churning the air around is known as *surging*. In mild cases the engine may continue to run at a reduced output but when the stall is more general the combustion chambers are starved of air and the engine stops. Conditions during surging can be very rough with a frightening increase in noise and a very rapid rise in the temperature at the compressor delivery; the rate at which the temperature rises is so marked that it can be used as an early warning that surge is beginning to take place. Today surging is virtually unheard of with a centrifugal compressor, but it can still prove a difficult problem with high-pressure axial compressors.

Compared with the sort of compression that takes place when air is forced into a cylinder head and held there by a piston, the operation carried out in a rotary compressor is much more hazardous; the air has to be driven along against a rising pressure with the ever-present risk that the flow may reverse if a very fine balance is disturbed. It is rather unfortunate that the critical conditions are quite likely to occur at the very high pressures that have to be used to give acceptable efficiency.

To a first order of magnitude the pressure ratio of a centrifugal compressor is related to its rotational speed. Overall performance and efficiency are also obviously related to its shape. Early impellers were machined from aluminium alloy. Today many centrifugal impellers are made of titanium, and this enables the shape to be improved while at the same time running at much higher r.p.m. in order to achieve pressure ratios around 10. Today's impellers curve the air smoothly around a gentle curve of large radius, ending in the desired radial direction. The high strength/weight ratio of titanium makes it possible for the air channels to be curved all the way to the periphery.

43. Compressor Characteristics

As it is essential to know the conditions under which individual compressor types are liable to surge so that these conditions may be avoided if at all possible, tests are carried out to determine the relationship between pressure ratio and mass flow at speeds covering the whole working range of the compressors, and the results are recorded on a series of curves known as *characteristics*. In Fig. 26 only

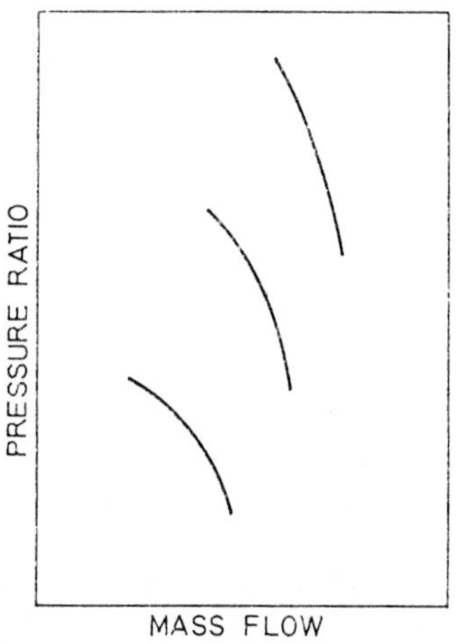

Fig. 26 Compressor characteristics

Variation of pressure ratio to mass flow, for three different speeds of the compressor

three typical curves are shown so as not to complicate the diagram. Each of the curves is obtained by running the compressor at a constant speed and observing the pressure ratio as the flow is decreased. The results shown seem quite reasonable and no mathematical proof is needed to confirm the idea that if there is less air flowing a given energy input will produce a higher final pressure. (The work done in compressing the air depends on the product of mass flow, inlet temperature, specific heat, and pressure ratio; since the specific heat and the inlet temperature are not likely to change in the course of an experiment, a decrease in the mass flow must result in an increase in the pressure ratio.) Reducing the mass flow reduces the radial velocity of the air beween the impeller blades and changes the angle at which the resultant airflow meets the diffuser blades. Ultimately a mass flow is reached which alters the angle the air makes to the diffuser blades to such an extent that the flow becomes turbulent. The point at which turbulence becomes severe is marked by a rapid drop in pressure and a sharp increase in noise. The tests are repeated at various speeds until the working range of the compressor has been covered.

Compressors with very modest pressure ratios have flat characteristics and are much more stable than compressors with high pressure ratios and steep characteristics. It is not difficult to see the sense of this as any tendency for the flow to reverse increases as the pressure goes up.

44. The Two-Stage Centrifugal Compressor

The first step towards improving the efficiency by raising the pressure ratio is to use a two-stage centrifugal compressor as successfully applied in the case of the Rolls-Royce Dart engine shown in diagrammatic arrangement in Fig. 22 and Plate 18. Air from the first stage of the compressor is fed back to the eye of the second impeller and given further compression in the next stage. The resulting pressure is about seven times the intake pressure at the first stage and represents a worthwhile increase compared with the $3\frac{1}{2}$ or 4 to 1 pressure ratio of a single stage when the Dart was designed in 1945. Any heating or turbulence occurring in the first stage detracts from the efficiency of the second and calls for careful design to eliminate as many losses as possible. The performance of the Dart and its very widespread acceptance show how successful this type of engine can be made.

Because of the mechanical simplicity of the compressor it is very robust so that the engine is able to swallow dust and small stones without suffering serious damage. The fairly low pressure ratios available result in relatively heavy fuel consumption, and limit the altitude at which the engine can operate successfully without risk of flame extinction through inadequate pressure in the combustion chamber.

Because of the radial flow through the centrifugal compressor this type is usually of greater diameter than an axial engine of comparable performance. The two-stage compressors and the double-sided impellers (Fig. 19) which were featured in the original Whittle engines and in their immediate Rolls-Royce descendants did not offend too badly in this respect but some of the engines which used single-sided centrifugal compressors took up a lot of room. The air entering the rear of the double-sided impeller had to turn back on its tracks to get in, but this was not at all serious as the engines ran in a nacelle which trapped the air and built up some pressure by ram; the engines did not appear to suffer from the tortuous path the air had to follow. Other successful engines of that era had even more complicated layouts with the compressor intakes half-way along the engine and hidden behind a festoon of pipes and combustion chambers which surrounded the compressor. At the speeds reached by these engines intake conditions were not critical, unlike present-day aircraft capable of very high speeds.

45. Axial Compressors

Since even the two-stage centrifugal compressor does not give very high pressure ratios, recourse is had to much more elaborate machines when the demand for performance can only be met by using higher pressure ratios. The demand arises from the need for higher efficiencies and the ability to maintain sufficient pressure inside the combustion chamber to support combustion at very high altitudes.

An axial compressor is shown diagrammatically in Fig. 27, and

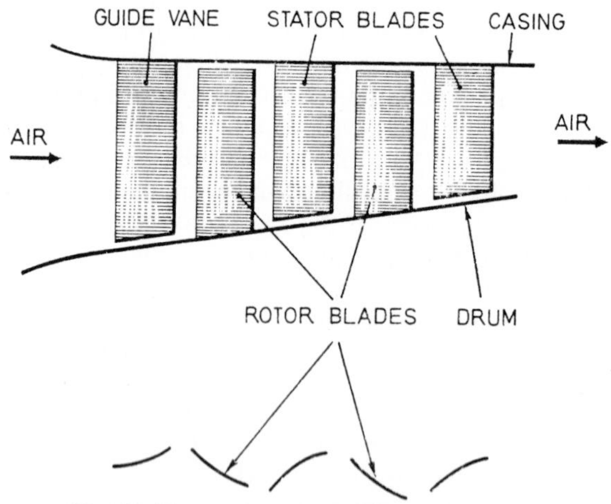

Fig. 27 Two stages of an axial compressor

Plate 19 conveys a good impression of what the rotor looks like. In these machines the air is given kinetic energy in successive rows of moving blades, called rotor blades, which are so shaped as to provide divergent passages between the blades in the same row. In this way the air leaves the rows of moving blades with some increase in kinetic energy and with a pressure rise due to the motion in the divergent passages. Each row of moving blades passes the air to a row of stationary blades, called stator blades. These provide divergent passages in which the speed of the air is reduced and the pressure further built up. It is possible for the air to leave the stationary blades with the same velocity as it entered the moving blades, all the kinetic energy imparted to it having been accounted for in the pressure increase. The combination of a row of moving blades and the following row of stator blades constitutes one stage. By increasing the pressure a little at a time in a number of stages, and doing it efficiently, it is possible to achieve far higher pressure ratios than can be obtained in a centrifugal machine of one or two stages.

On some compressors a row of guide vanes is fixed to the casing in front of the first row of moving blades. These guide vanes deflect the air in the direction in which the blades are moving to minimize shock at entry. By mounting the guide vanes so that they may be swivelled about their own axes they can be set, whilst the engine is running if necessary, to suit the different conditions that develop as the engine is run up to normal speed after starting. The full significance of these guide vanes will become clearer when the appropriate diagrams are studied later.

It is usual for each stage of the compressor to give an equal amount of whirl to the air, although there may be no very compelling reason why this should be so. As the axial velocity of the air is kept reasonably constant from intake to outlet, the annular space between drum and casing is progressively reduced in size to suit the increased density of the air. Each row of blades is designed for the task it has to do, and although each stage may raise the pressure by the same amount the blades differ in length, shape and possibly in material from row to row.

To get a clear idea of how air is compressed it is better to trace the changes that take place as the air passes from the leading edges of the guide vanes to the outlet from the first row of stator blades. Normal running conditions will be considered first and the more difficult problem of how to start the compressor running will be considered later.

46. Compressor Velocity Diagrams

Figure 28 shows, from left to right, a guide vane followed by a moving blade and stator blade of the first stage of a compressor. The guide vane deflects the air in the direction of the compressor rotation so that it is travelling in the direction V_{ai} when it meets the moving

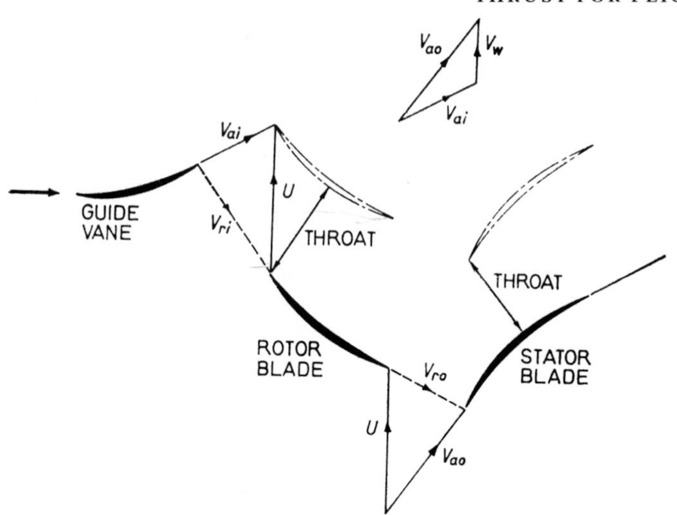

Fig. 28 Velocity triangles

Symbols

U represents velocity of rotor blade
V_{ai} represents absolute velocity of air at rotor inlet
V_{ao} represents absolute velocity of air at rotor outlet
V_{ri} represents relative velocity of air to rotor blade at rotor inlet
V_{ro} represents relative velocity of air to rotor blade at rotor outlet
V_w represents whirl velocity added to V_{ai} to give V_{ao}

blade. This deflection of the air in the direction in which the blade is moving gives it a velocity relative to the blade of V_{ri}, which is less than it would have been if the air had been flowing straight in at right-angles to the plane of rotation. The leading edges of the moving blades are set so as to receive the air flowing in the direction V_{ri} and the passages formed between blades in the same row widen to give divergent channels. In these divergent passages the relative air speed is reduced and the pressure increased as described in Section 40 for a duct forced through the air. The air caught up between the rotor blades is given a whirl velocity V_w which results in it having a velocity V_{ao} when it leaves the blades. Because of the blade movement the relative velocity of the air to the blade is V_{ro} at the outlet. Notice that the relative velocity has actually decreased, hence the rise in pressure within the rotor blade ring, although the absolute velocity has been increased by the work done on the air. The trailing edge of the moving blade is set to suit the velocity V_{ro} relative to the blade, and the leading edge of the stator blade is set to accept air flowing in the direction of V_{ao}, which is the absolute velocity of the air at the rotor blade outlet. The stator blade is curved so that the air leaves the trailing edge in the direction of V_{ai} and ready to start the treatment all over again in the next stage. The air is back to the velocity it had at the entry to the first stage but the pressure is higher by an amount depending on the kinetic energy given to the air and on the efficiency of conversion.

The three triangles of Fig. 28 may be combined in a single diagram as in Fig. 29 because the triangles share common velocities. In this

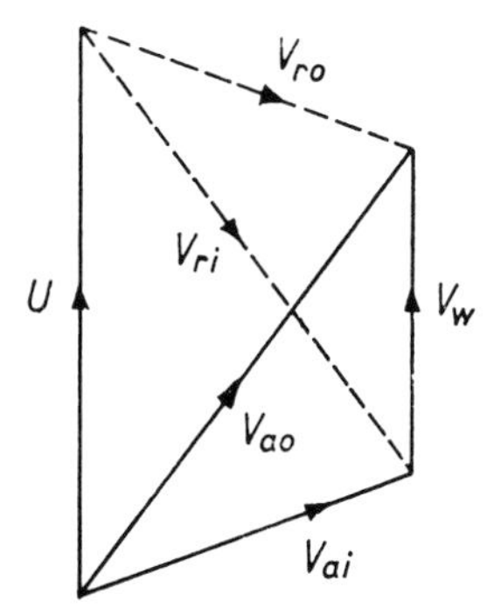

Fig. 29 Combined velocity diagram showing symmetrical conditions in which inlet and outlet triangles are identical

particular case the diagram happens to be a symmetrical one, indicating that the deflection applied to the air and the velocity changes that follow are the same for rotor and stator blades. Since the difference between the two relative velocities is numerically the same as the difference between the two absolute velocities the indications are that the moving blades and the stator blades contribute equally to the pressure rise. This arrangement has much in its favour, as the velocity changes are less violent than in a stage in which there is more pressure rise, and more velocity change, in one half of the stage than in the other.

The shape of the rotor blades is determined by the angles V_{ri} and V_{ro} make to the plane of rotation. Similarly the shape of the stator blades is fixed by the angles made by V_{ao} and V_{ai} to the plane of rotation. The situation depicted is for one station only, say half-way along the blade length at the section usually referred to as the *blade mean height*. At the blade root and at the tip, speeds due to rotation differ from the speed at mean height and in consequence the angles assumed by the airflow relative to the blades differ at all stations along the blades.

47. Free Vortex Flow

The blade shape is also influenced by the pattern of flow which air or any other fluid takes up naturally as it whirls along inside a pipe. In this *free vortex flow* every particle follows a helical path, neither increasing nor decreasing its distance from the axis of rotation and advancing at the same rate as all other particles which were in the same plane initially. Radial flow due to centrifugal force is prevented by a build-up of pressure from the inner to the outer radius. The situation is very similar to what takes place when liquid in a cup is stirred vigorously; the level rises towards the rim of the cup and falls towards the centre, so that at any chosen level in the liquid the pressures at points away from the centre are higher than at the centre because of the increased depth of liquid above these points. This example might be regarded as free vortex flow in the special case where there is no axial velocity.

When free vortex flow exists, the pressure must be greater at larger radii than it is near the axis and some source of energy must be tapped to provide it. There is kinetic energy available both because the air is flowing and because it is whirling, but since there must be no change in axial velocity the kinetic energy due to whirl is the one that must change, and vary from the centre onwards. Near the axis the whirl velocity is high, but it becomes less as the radius is increased. This is so as to provide the drop in kinetic energy that produces the increase in pressure which counteracts the effects of centrifugal force. The relationship is fairly simple as the whirl velocity is inversely proportional to the radius.

The effect of free vortex flow on blade shape is shown in Fig. 30. At blade mean height the diagram is symmetrical, indicating that the pressure build-up is shared equally between the rotor and stator rings. Starting with the symmetrical conditions at mean height, the diagrams for root and tip are easily derived by changing the whirl velocity component in inverse proportion to the distance the root and tip are from the centre of rotation. This matter is mentioned as an indication that not all calculations involved are very abstruse; the trouble sometimes lies in the vast number of them.

It will be noticed that in addition to twisting from root to tip the blade also undergoes a considerable change in *camber*, that is, the blade is much more curved at the root than at the tip. Because of the complicated shape the blade is not particularly easy to make. The

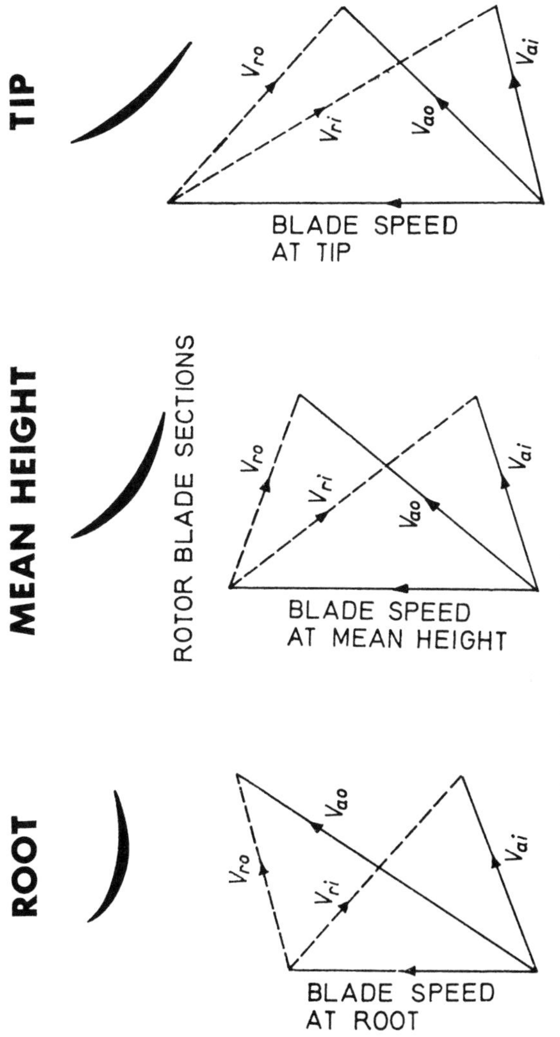

Fig. 30 Velocity triangles for a free vortex flow blade

excessive curvature at the root may lead to break-away of the airflow, and relative velocities at the tip may become high enough to cause shock losses. These things only happen when the blade is worked to the limits; if the pressure ratio expected of it is not too high the blade will perform perfectly.

48. Constant Reaction Blades

Most engineering problems are solved by reaching a compromise and this is certainly true when deciding on the blade shape for any particular compressor application. It is possible to produce shapes that are more effective than the free vortex blade in raising the pressure, but which have steeper characteristics and will only give satisfactory running over a narrower range.

In this category there is the *constant reaction blade*, a title which should simply be accepted for the present as its significance will become clearer when the term 'reaction' is used in connection with the turbine to which it really belongs. These constant reaction blades are exactly the same as the free vortex blades at the mean height and impart the same amount of whirl at the root and tip as is the case with the free vortex blade. The real difference lies in the blade angles, which are chosen to give symmetrical diagrams all the way up the blade as shown in Fig. 31. A blade of this shape has less camber at the root and more moderate relative velocities at the tip but, because of the blade angles chosen, air which has free vortex flow meets the blades at larger angles of attack. This means that the blades are working closer to the stalling angle, hence the steeper characteristics. Other compromise blades exist which are designed to give higher pressures than could be obtained by complying with free vortex flow conditions, and it may be that for some specific purpose the extra power to drive and the more critical conditions involved are justified.

49. Stall and Surge

In Section 9, when dealing with the airflow over a propeller blade, mention was made of the fact that if the angle of attack becomes excessive the air no longer follows the curved surface smoothly but breaks away and the flow becomes turbulent. When this happens a lot of energy is wasted in the creation of eddies and less is available for the intended purpose. If the aerofoil is a wing, lift is lost and the drag resulting from the turbulence may reduce forward speed enough to

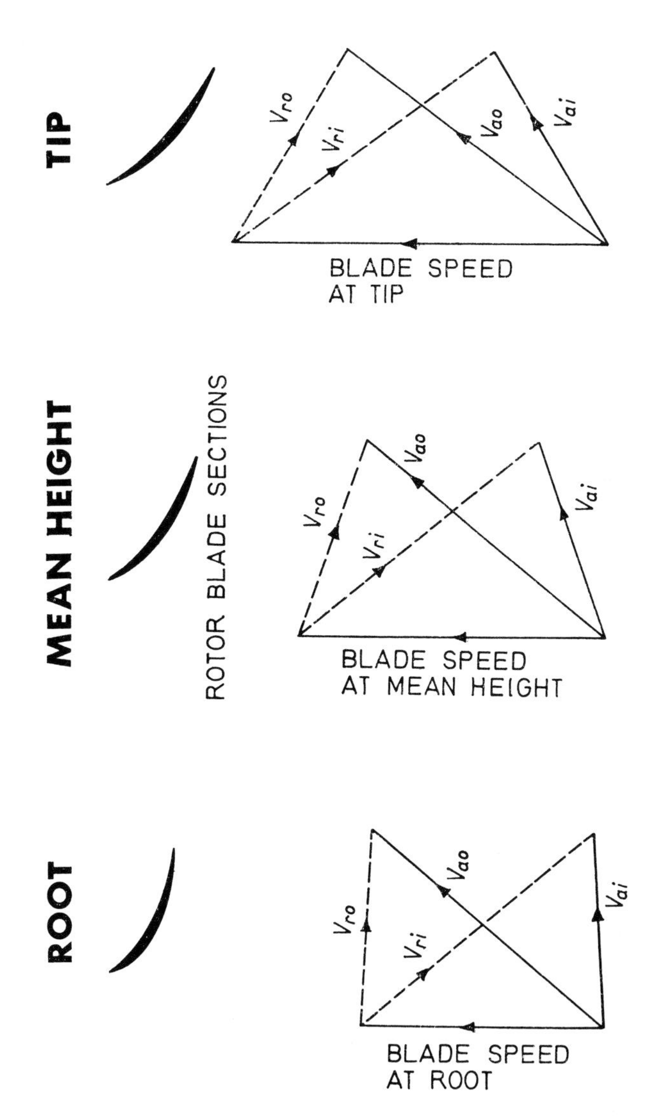

Fig. 31 Velocity triangles for a constant reaction blade

Note reduced curvature of blade at root compared with free vortex blade and reduced value of V_{rt}

cause disaster. In the case of compressor blades, stalling may reduce or interrupt the flow of air to the combustion chambers and starve the engine with the result that it stops. Normally things are not quite as bad as that, for the stall does not affect all the blades in a row at the same time and some of the passages may handle enough air to keep the engine running. Observations made in Perspex models show that the stall moves round the annulus, so that as one passage reverts to smooth flow another stalls and so on in a rhythmic sequence. Blade vibration may have something to do with the initiation of stall, for when operating somewhere near the stall the 'downwards' flick of vibrating blades adds another component to the relative velocity which may be sufficient to bring on the stalled condition.

Partial stalling may take place without noticeable loss of performance, but when it becomes widespread there may be sufficient stalling and reverse flow to starve the combustion chambers and cause a flameout – extinction of the flame whilst the engine continues to windmill. Some forms of compressor stall can be initiated by manoeuvres whilst flying, but most occur when starting or accelerating the engine.

50. Starting the Airflow

The proportions of a compressor annulus are designed for handling air at the pressures to be expected under normal running conditions, and therefore there is a contraction of the air passage from front to rear to suit the smaller volume of air to be handled at the outlet. Unfortunately, when the compressor is run up to start the engine there is at first very little pressure rise and consequently very little reduction in volume, and the air travels faster and faster through the narrowing gap. The speed becomes so great that *choking* may occur, and for once we have a technical term that means just what most people assume it to do. When the speed of sound is reached the air cannot be made to travel any faster by the application of more pressure and the earlier stages stall because they cannot get rid of enough air to keep up a satisfactory rate of flow. The early axial compressors were reasonably free from surge because the pressure ratios were not very high, but the trouble became progressively worse as more and more stages were added.

So as to get pressure ratios high enough to give reasonable thermal efficiencies by providing adequate expansion ratios, it is necessary to accept various complications usually incorporated to get the air moving when the engine is being started.

51. Adjustable Guide Vanes

One solution is to have a row of adjustable guide vanes so that, by pivoting these in their sockets, the incoming air may be whirled in the direction of rotation and the relative velocity at the rotor blades changed in a way that reduces the angle of attack and the risk of stall. As the vanes are moved they close the gap through which the air is flowing and restrict the flow to an amount that the rear stages can swallow without choking. Almost all modern high-pressure engines have VIGVs (variable inlet guide vanes) and often from one to eight additional stages of variable stators all linked together and driven by a hydraulic ram via rings around the compressor casings (Fig. 52). The benefits that come from the use of these and other devices for avoiding stall must be carefully considered in the light of cost unless it is impossible to start the airflow without them.

52. Blow-off Valves

Another way of easing the problems of starting a high-pressure axial compressor is to fit it with blow-off valves. As the basic problem is that the air coming in at the front cannot get out at the back it is sensible to provide holes in the casing through which a proportion of the air can escape. The size, position and even exact shape of these holes is very important, and they have to be fitted with valves which shut them off as the engine runs up to speed and the compressor begins operating normally. Some engines have both blow-off valves and variable inlet vanes.

53. Two-Spool Compressors

Almost all modern fighter and airline engines have at least two independent rotating systems. The commonest, the two-spool arrangement, comprises a small HP (high-pressure) compressor driven by an HP turbine, and a much larger LP (low-pressure) compressor or fan driven by a LP turbine via a shaft passing down the centre of the tubular HP shaft. This enormously eases the problems, especially during starting when only the HP spool is externally driven. This gets the airflow going and the fuel burners lit, and the resulting flow of hot gas then runs up the LP spool. As explained in Section 74 the HP turbine operates in intensely hot high-energy gas and may have only a single stage, whereas the much larger LP turbine may need five or six stages (Fig. 53).

Rolls-Royce has been the champion of the three-shaft engine, for both large subsonic airline engines and supersonic military jets. They claim three-spool engines can be shorter, more rigid and more efficient than equivalent two-shaft engines ('spool' and 'shaft' are synonymous in this context), and also over a period of years have better performance retention.

54. Temperature Effects

Compression inevitably results in an increase in the temperature of the air and any inefficiency in the compressor boosts it still further. The temperature after compression is of great importance, as it limits the amount of fuel that may be burned in the combustion chambers without overheating the turbine blades. Modern engines with a pressure ratio around 35 heat the air so much that the final stages of blades have to be of refractory (heat resisting) alloys similar to those used in turbines. The air enters the combustion chamber at about the same temperature as it *left* the combustion chambers of the first jet engines! Such a restriction on the amount of fuel limits the power available and is a point that must be carefully watched during the design and development stages – the search for higher efficiencies might in certain circumstances result in lower powers!

55. Fuels and Combustion

The requirements of aircraft engines are best met by the provision of liquid fuel, because of the ease with which it can be stored, transferred to aircraft tanks and piped to the engines. Petroleum, which provides the bulk of aircraft fuels, is mineral in origin and is raised from wells by pumping or by the gas pressure which often exists within the wells. The crude oil as it comes from the wells is of little use as a fuel until it has been subjected to complicated refining and manufacturing processes to rid it of impurities and to separate the constituents from one another. The separation is done by distillation which drives off the lighter elements at the lower temperatures and the heavier elements as the temperature is raised. The fuels in the order in which they are driven off as the temperature is raised are petrol (for use in piston engines), white spirit, kerosene (widely used in gas turbines), gas oil (for use in diesel engines) and furnace oil for burning in steam raising plants and other applications where a high degree of refinement is not called for.

Many of the properties required of the fuels are more easily studied in relationship to their uses, for although piston engines and turbines burn fuels which are very similar to one another the different conditions of burning and of operation generally demand separate consideration. The properties of major importance to the piston engine will be introduced first.

It is important that liquid fuels should be volatile as conversion to the gaseous state must take place before burning. When carburettors are used to supply the fuel it is widely believed that it is best to complete the evaporation before the mixture enters the cylinders, otherwise there is a risk that the cylinders will not receive an equal share of the fuel or of some of the additives put in to improve certain aspects of performance. Later, in Section 57 something will be said about these additives and how they work, but it is interesting at this stage to look at the problem of sharing out the tiny quantities of these substances to the cylinders. One of the best-known additives is tetraethyl lead which increases resistance to detonation but which must be supplied along with ethylene dibromide to counteract the ill effects of the lead. The ethylene dibromide tends to evaporate with the lighter elements of the fuel leaving the tetraethyl lead behind with the liquid fuel. When evaporation in the induction system is incomplete, distribution of the remaining liquid between the cylinders is seldom in equal shares. This can result in some cylinders being deprived of tetraethyl lead and suffering from detonation whilst others are supplied with too much tetraethyl lead and not enough ethylene dibromide to safeguard the valves from lead deposits. If the distribution is not right an excellent fuel may do more harm than good, so besides deciding which fuel properties are desirable it is also important to appreciate how the fuels should be used.

Starting from cold, particularly extreme cold, may present difficulties with fuels of low volatility unless steps are taken either to heat the engine, prime the cylinders with highly volatile fuels, or dilute the lubricating oil so that the crankshaft may be spun more briskly to improve the prospects of getting a start (a fast cranking speed helps both the carburettor and the ignition system to work properly and there is less time for the fuels to condense in the cylinders). A fuel of high volatility helps the starting process by vaporizing readily, but this same quality may result in vapour forming where it is not wanted in the pipelines and passages of the fuel supply system to such an extent that the flow of fuel is obstructed.

56. Combustion in the Piston Engine

Whilst the fuel properties mentioned in the previous section are of vital importance it must be remembered that the main purpose of feeding fuel to the engine is to get it to release heat, so the conditions conducive to effective combustion must be understood. Naturally it is expected that every trace of combustible matter is used up and that the engine design is such that a worth-while proportion of the heat is converted to mechanical energy. The way in which the mixture of fuel and air burns in the cylinder depends to some extent on the proportions of fuel and air in the mixture and certain standard mixtures are recognized as a basis for discussions on performance.

A *correct mixture* of fuel and air is one in which there is just the right amount of air to burn the fuel completely and leave no unconsumed oxygen in the products of combustion. When a correct mixture is completely burned the exhaust gases consist of steam (formed by the combination of hydrogen from the fuel with oxygen from the air), carbon dioxide (formed by the combination of carbon from the fuel with oxygen from the air), and nitrogen.

A *weak mixture* is one in which there is more air than the minimum required to complete combustion. In such a mixture it is usual for all trace of combustible matter from the fuel to burn up completely, leaving some unconsumed oxygen in the exhaust. The weak mixtures would appear to be just what is required for economy and within limits this is so, but like many another good thing it can be overdone. Too weak a mixture carries through the engine a large excess of air which has to be compressed and pushed out again without contributing to the useful work. A weak mixture also burns slowly and allows the piston to pass t.d.c. before combustion is completed, so that the maximum pressure is less than it would have been if all combustion had been completed before t.d.c. In extreme cases of weak-mixture running the gases may still be burning when the exhaust valves open, so exposing the valves to much higher temperatures than would have prevailed with complete combustion before expansion. It is this slow burning that accounts for signs of overheating with weak mixtures, as a certain amount of the heat never gets a chance to be converted to work by expansion and has to be carried away by the cooling system.

A *rich mixture* is one in which there is not enough oxygen to unite with all the fuel and some combustible matter is carried away unconsumed in the exhaust system. Naturally a volatile fuel like petrol does not survive as a liquid in the furnace-like conditions of the combustion chambers; what usually happens is that there is insufficient oxygen for all the carbon to yield carbon dioxide and some carbon monoxide appears in the exhaust. If there had been plenty of oxygen the carbon monoxide would have united with it to form carbon dioxide and in the process it would have released quite a bit more heat. In the case of extremely rich mixtures carbon, in the form of soot or black smoke, can be seen coming from the exhaust.

In spite of the apparent wastefulness of rich mixtures they are used deliberately in certain running conditions. When full power is needed, for example, it is usual to supply a slightly rich mixture so as to ensure that every trace of oxygen is used up and the maximum heat extracted from the mixture taken into the engine. The power of an engine really depends on the amount of air that it swallows per minute and it is essential that all the air be made to contribute to it. In a subsequent section it will be shown that it is not an easy matter to increase the air consumption beyond a certain amount, hence the anxiety to make full use of all that does get in. As the evaporation of fuel takes up heat from its surroundings, the excess fuel does a useful job by helping to cool the inside of the cylinders at a time when the cooling system is on full stretch because the engine is developing maximum power.

At the other end of the power scale, when the engine is idling, a slightly rich mixture is again supplied because in this running condition there may be only enough heat to evaporate the lighter elements of the fuel and without the excess fuel there would not be enough vapour available at the right time. Depending on the length and shape of the manifolds, certain cylinders may be starved of fuel or receive only heavier unevaporated elements unless the supply is generous enough to make sure that every cylinder gets sufficient vapour to start combustion.

Inevitably some of the heat of combustion passes to the components which are exposed to the flames, and as the gas temperatures are high enough to burn valves, valve seats, sparking plugs and pistons, arrangements must be made to remove heat from these parts and transfer it to the coolant and the cooling air. As the heat carried away by the cooling system has done no useful work everything possible must be done to minimize it. A compact combustion chamber with the minimum amount of metal surrounding the gases reduces the path through which heat may pass, and the flow of coolant should be no more than is absolutely necessary to keep the vulnerable parts at a safe temperature. Overcooling only increases loss of heat and it may also cause condensation inside the engine, contaminating the oil and increasing the rate of wear.

As the spark that starts the burning is usually timed to take place about 20 degrees before t.d.c., combustion has a good chance of being completed before the piston has moved very far along the power stroke. The heat energy in the gas is reduced during the power stroke by the amount of work done on the piston and it would seem good business to reduce the store of heat as much as possible in this way. However, in a conventional engine the use of a high expansion ratio to exploit the heat in the gases involves the use of an equally high compression ratio. For example if the gases in the clearance volume at the beginning of the power stroke are expanded to ten times that volume in an effort to make the best use of the heat, the fresh charge will in due course have to be compressed to one-tenth of the volume occupied at the beginning of the compression stroke. High compression ratios, adopted because of the benefit obtained from a high expansion ratio, result in high temperatures at the end of compression. Since the mixture of fuel and air is a combustible one, there is a limit to how much heat may be added by compression without giving rise to a condition in which combustion takes place with explosive violence.

57. Detonation and Octane Ratings

Normally, when combustion has been started by the spark, the flame spreads steadily through the mixture as the advancing flame front heats the gases immediately ahead of it, so that they in turn burn too. Progressively there is more and more heat concentrated in the flame front, which is brought to bear on the remaining *end gas*. Ultimately there is enough heat available to bring all the end gas to the point of combustion at the same moment and it explodes with a degree of violence which depends on how much end gas has been subjected to heating and pressure. The amount of end gas may vary from practically nothing in certain combustion chambers in lightly loaded engines to the whole clearance volume when totally unsuitable fuels are used in adverse conditions. Detonation involving the whole of the clearance volume would almost certainly wreck a normal engine.

In addition to the noise, which is objectionable in itself, the sudden rise in pressure that occurs with detonation applies a shock load to the engine parts and may reduce power by acting on the piston as it rises to t.d.c. Normally, there is a *boundary layer* of gas over the piston crown, at roughly the crown temperature, which protects the crown from excess heat. The shock wave set up by the explosion sweeps the boundary layer from the piston crown and exposes the metal to the intense heat of the flame. If detonation is allowed to persist, failure of the metal is likely to follow. When the majority of the cylinders are affected, detonation makes its presence known by the noise and loss of power, and adjustments can be made to the control settings before any damage is done; but if only a minority of the cylinders are detonating the noise may be covered up by the general uproar that goes with the generation of high powers. Much damage can be done in a case like this, for the detonation may go unnoticed until it is too late.

A knowledge of the factors likely to promote detonation is worth acquiring. Any condition that heats the charge before combustion will aggravate matters in the end gas; pre-heating the air before it enters the engine or over-compression in the supercharger may well give rise to excessive temperatures. Once the burning has actually started the process should not be prolonged, as detonation is caused by certain organic peroxides which act as fulminates to explode the end gas. The formation of these peroxides takes time, so that anything that can reduce the time needed to burn the charge reduces the possibility of detonation taking place. A compact combustion chamber helps in this respect by reducing the distance the flame front has to travel, and the time taken to burn the charge can be reduced by initiating flame fronts from several sparking plugs at the same time. Turbulence induced in the charge can increase the rate of burning by breaking up the flame front and exposing more fresh charge for burning. If possible the flame should be started from the vicinity of some hot spot such as the exhaust valve so that the flame pushes the end gas away from the hot zone and compresses it into a cooler one. Before the advent of really good fuels rendered such expedients unnecessary some combustion chambers were designed with cool spaces into which the end gas was forced.

So far the steps taken to delay the onset of detonation have been questions of design, but running conditions can also be chosen to give favourable conditions for detonation-free running. For example, the same power may be obtained at a higher engine speed by using a lower gear or a finer propeller pitch so that a smaller throttle opening is used at higher r.p.m. This helps in two ways: the reduced throttle opening diminishes the maximum cylinder pressure, and the higher speed cuts down the time available for peroxide formation. If it is impossible to keep up the power by increasing the r.p.m. at a smaller throttle opening, detonation may be kept at bay by closing the throttle slightly to reduce the cylinder pressure; this results in a drop in power which may be no worse than the drop which would occur with detonation. Retardation of the spark may reduce a tendency to detonate by delaying the build-up of pressure in the cylinder, but it also cuts down the power.

High-power engines in World War II were often equipped for water injection. Water, or a 50/50 mixture with methanol, was sprayed into the eye of the supercharger, to cool the charge (which increased its density and thus also the power) and eliminate detonation.

By far the neatest way of controlling detonation is by improving the quality of the fuel. This may be done by blending with various components produced by very accurate processes and especially by adding a small proportion of TEL (tetra-ethyl lead). TEL prevents the formation of the peroxides but has to be used with care because of the corrosive effects on exhaust valves and seats. The use of ethylene dibromide neutralizes the corrosive effects of the lead, and valves made from corrosion-resisting steels go a long way towards solving this problem. Today lead is recognized as a dangerously cumulative health hazard, and there is strong pressure to standardize on lead-free fuels.

As soon as detonation was recognized as one of the most serious obstacles to further progress for the spark ignition petrol engine (diesels are not affected in this way), intensive research was carried out by Ricardo and others. This resulted in the development of ingenious and comprehensively equipped engines in which almost everything, except the bore and stroke, can be varied whilst the engine is running. With these engines it is possible to observe, under carefully controlled conditions, the effect on detonation of changes in compression ratio, ignition timing, mixture strength, and inlet temperature.

When it became necessary to establish standards by which fuels could be judged or specified these engines were adapted for the purpose. The standard chosen for resistance to detonation was the performance of iso-octane because at that time it was considered that this substance was better than any fuel likely to be produced commercially. The iso-octane is used in conjunction with heptane, which has little or no resistance to detonation, to produce reference fuels to serve as samples. During the test of a fuel the engine is run under specified conditions and the compression ratio is raised until detonation occurs; blends are then made up of iso-octane and heptane until one is found that gives the same resistance to knocking as the fuel under test. The fuel is then allocated an *octane number* which is the percentage of iso-octane in the blend of iso-octane and heptane. For example, a fuel of 95 octane rating has the same resistance to detonation as a blend of 95 per cent iso-octane and 5 per cent heptane.

The original tests for octane rating were based on the air-to-fuel ratio which gave maximum knocking, but this condition is not truly representative of the whole working range. Maximum knocking occurs with slightly weak mixtures which are about right for cruising, but as rich mixtures are used for take-off and climbing it is important to know how the fuel behaves under these exacting conditions. Up to a point, the anti-knock performance of all the usual fuels increases with increase in mixture strength, although the amount of the increase is not the same for all fuels. When fuels are listed with two ratings the lower refers to the weak-mixture performance and the higher to what is achieved with rich mixtures; when only one rating is given this refers to the weak-mixture performance. It is important to realize that two fuels with the same weak-mixture rating may perform quite differently in the rich-mixture condition. This is why car owners sometimes find that one brand of fuel suits their engines better than another brand with the same octane number.

In the course of time fuels became available with better anti-knock properties than iso-octane and to rate these, comparisons are made with fuels composed of iso-octane doped with tetraethyl lead.

An alternative scale for rating fuels which have a very high resistance to knocking is provided by the range of *performance numbers.* These state the power given by the fuel as a percentage of the power obtained when using a standard reference fuel under exactly the same conditions.

58. Gas-Turbine Fuels

The foregoing paragraphs have concentrated on the fuel properties needed to get the best performance from high-powered piston engines. The gas turbine has a somewhat different set of requirements arising from the fact that it is more likely to be called upon to operate at extreme altitudes involving very low temperatures, and it also has to burn the fuel under conditions quite different from those in the piston engine. Existing fuels such as kerosene and low-grade petrol can produce all the heat that the materials of construction can stand, so there is no question of engine development being held up for lack of a suitable fuel as has happened from time to time in the piston-engine field.

One effect of extremely low temperature is to start the formation of wax crystals in the fuel. Whilst most pumps are able to slice through the wax, pipelines and filters tend to clog. In some aircraft the formation of wax can be avoided by placing the pipelines and filters where there is sufficient heat from the engine, and in others where the aircraft speed is high enough kinetic heating may provide the solution. The present generation, which has heard so much about the risk of burning that threatens satellites which re-enter the atmosphere at excessive speeds, needs no introduction to the term kinetic heating; fast aircraft are just on the fringe of this problem and can take advantage of the heat to ensure wax-free fuel.

The fuel used in aircraft turbines must burn quickly so as to keep the length of the combustion chamber and the overall length of the engine as short as possible. Comparison between some early designs and those currently in use shows that in spite of greatly increased outputs, development has resulted in combustion chambers much shorter than they were. Kerosene happens to meet the requirement of quick burning and was the obvious choice in the pioneering days. It might still be first choice if there was plenty of it, but kerosene is only 6 per cent of the yield from crude petroleum and *long cut fuels* have had to be used to supplement supplies. These long-cut (or wide-cut) fuels have a much wider boiling range than kerosene and are in fact akin to low-octane gasolines and diesel fuels.

Good volatility in the fuel is desirable because this simplifies starting and gives efficient burning with a stable flame; rapid ignition in cold conditions ensures that liquid fuel does not collect in nooks and crannies to catch fire in the wrong places when ignition finally takes place in the combustion chambers. Such wet starts may send flames shooting through the turbine and expose the blades to temperatures they were never expected to stand. Against the advantages of highly volatile fuels must be weighed the risk of vapour locks in the pipelines and the losses by evaporation which can reach unexpected levels. The high rates of climb now possible particularly with combat aircraft, mean that high altitudes and low atmospheric pressures are reached before the fuel has had a chance to cool from sea-level temperatures; these conditions are conducive to boiling to an extent that may account for a 10 per cent fuel loss in a climb to 35,000 feet.

As already stated, fairly ordinary fuels produced from crude oils can release all the heat needed to give temperatures well beyond the limits that can safely be used with materials normally available at economic prices, but the fuel for long-range aircraft takes up so much space and represents such a large proportion of the total weight at take-off that no effort is spared in the search for fuel economy. When the engine manufacturers have done all they can with existing materials and techniques it is only logical to take a look at the fuels to see if they can be improved in any way. All the hydrocarbon fuels derived from crude oils have very similar calorific values and the only advantage of one fuel over another may be in respect of density; a high-density fuel occupies less space than one of lower density.

From time to time particular exotic fuels have been marketed, but none has become important. An example is Shelldyne, dating from 1959, which had a calorific value per unit volume about 30 per cent higher than common kerosenes, and thus could extend the range of fighters where the fuel capacity was limited by volume, not by weight. However, if the history of piston-engine fuels is anything to go by the exotic fuels of today are the normal fuels of tomorrow. Who would have thought in the years of World War II, when high-octane fuels were at a premium, that before many years had passed these same high-octane fuels and better, would be obtainable at roadside pumps and would become the normal requirement for high-performance mass-produced cars?

59. Supplying the Fuel to the Combustion Chambers

The whole question of supplying fuel to the combustion chambers in the right condition for burning and in the quantities necessary to give the power required, is a comprehensive one that cannot be handled in general terms, particularly when dealing with two different engine types. About the only things the two engines have in common concerning combustion are that the fuels must be vaporized and mixed with oxygen; evaporation and mixing with air is assisted by supplying the fuel in a very fine spray, and any heat given up by the metal parts in the process of evaporating the fuel helps to cool some very hot spots. Thereafter the task of getting the fuel to the burning zone differs so much between piston engines and turbines that separate descriptions for each are required. For both engine types the basic ideas are simple enough but the automatic devices and the various corrections that are applied add to the complications. The piston engine is dealt with first, because the simple carburettors of the low powered engines are very straightforward and seem to provide a natural introduction to the subject.

60. Induction

There are two recognized ways of getting the fresh charge of fuel and air into the cylinders of the piston engine: it may be drawn in by the depression created by the piston of the normally aspirated engine as shown in Fig. 32, or it may be forced in by means of a pump or supercharger as in Fig. 33. Fuel may be supplied by a choke tube carburettor (Fig. 32*a*), by individual injection to each cylinder (Fig. 32*b*) or by injection at the supercharger (Fig. 33). In each case the fuel supply must be closely related to the air consumption, with minor variations to suit individual running conditions.

61. The Simple Carburettor

The simple carburettor is a straightforward device for getting fuel into the induction system. It is almost completely free from moving parts and is capable of working for long periods without attention provided the fuel supply is properly filtered to prevent foreign matter

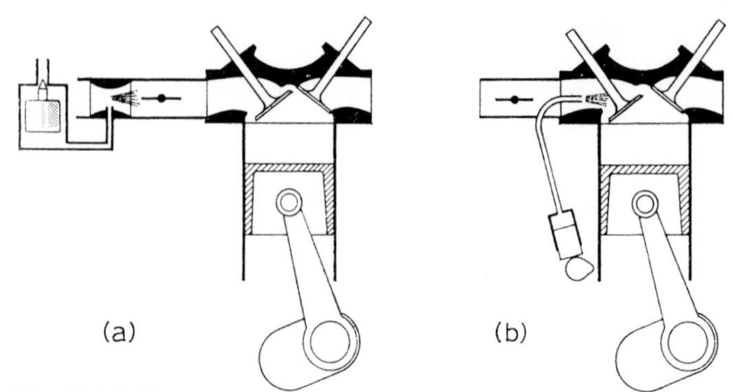

Fig. 32 (*a*) Normally aspirated engine with choke tube carburettor (*b*) Normally aspirated engine with pump injection to each cylinder

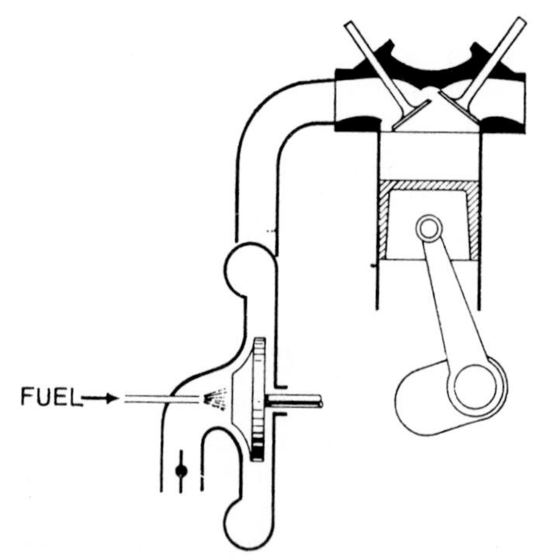

Fig. 33 Supercharged engine with fuel injection

in the fuel from reaching and blocking some of the small-bore passages that are a necessary feature of these instruments. In that shown in Fig. 34 the supply of mixture to the engine is regulated by the throttle, which is in the position A for full power and at B when the engine is idling. The choke is there to create a drop in pressure and cause fuel to flow from the float chamber in quantities approximately proportional to the air consumption. The float and needle valve prevent flooding when no fuel is required and maintain a reasonably steady level of fuel in the delivery tube when the engine is running.

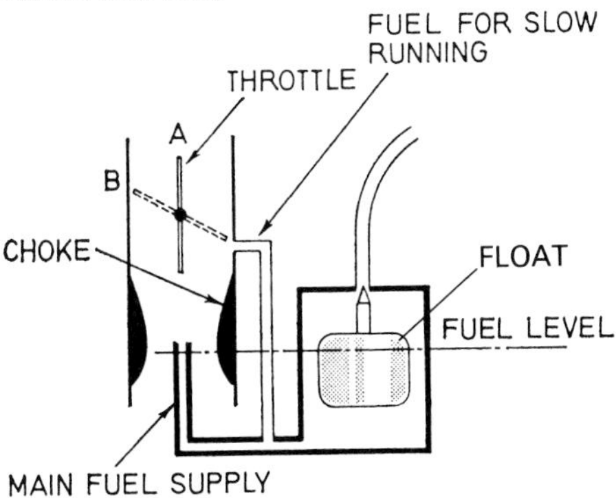

Fig. 34 Simple carburettor

The drop in pressure that occurs in the choke is explained by Bernouilli's theorem which in its simplest version states that when a fluid flows in a duct the total energy per pound remains unaltered unless the fluid is made to do work or has work done on it. The fluid possesses energy because of its pressure, temperature and motion; if one of these is changed, one or both of the others must change to compensate. In other words, when the speed increases at the narrow neck of the choke there will be a drop in pressure and in temperature which is proportional to the increase in speed. In the case of the carburettor the drop in temperature is not significant and no use is made of it, but the pressure drop is used to make fuel flow from the float chamber to the induction system.

Engines which have to run at only one speed and load may make do with a simple carburettor of the type shown in Fig. 34 but when provision has to be made for a variety of speeds and loads a rather more complicated carburettor is required. The reason why the simple carburettor cannot cover a wide working range is that if tuned to give a correct mixture at one particular speed it will deliver a very much richer mixture when running faster and a weaker mixture when running slower.

At the lower end of the speed range, when turning the crankshaft to start the engine, there is not enough pressure drop to get the fuel flowing, and other arrangements have to be made for the fuel supply to suit the starting and slow-running conditions in which the throttle is almost closed. The small quantity of air swallowed by the engine in these conditions has to travel fast to pass through the gap between the throttle plate and the body of the carburettor, and in so doing it sets up a zone of low pressure which serves to draw fuel from the float chamber and feed it to the induction pipe. The action at the edge of the throttle plate is vigorous enough to break up the fuel into tiny droplets which vaporize readily.

Once the engine has been started on this auxiliary jet the throttle may be opened progressively, and as the speed increases the rush of air through the choke produces a sufficient drop in pressure to bring the main delivery tube into action. By the time this happens the throttle has moved so far from the body of the carburettor that it no longer creates a zone of low pressure at the slow-running jet, and delivery of fuel at this point ceases.

62. Compensating Devices

As has already been stated, increasing the flow of air through the carburettor beyond a certain amount results in a flow of fuel in excess of what is required to give a correct mixture. A compromise can be reached by sharing the total fuel flow between main and compensator jets; the main jet is subject at all times to the pressure difference between the choke and the surrounding atmosphere, but the compensator jet works differently. Although the flow from the main jet increases with increase in engine speed, the maximum flow with the arrangement shown in Fig. 35 is less than for the single jet shown in

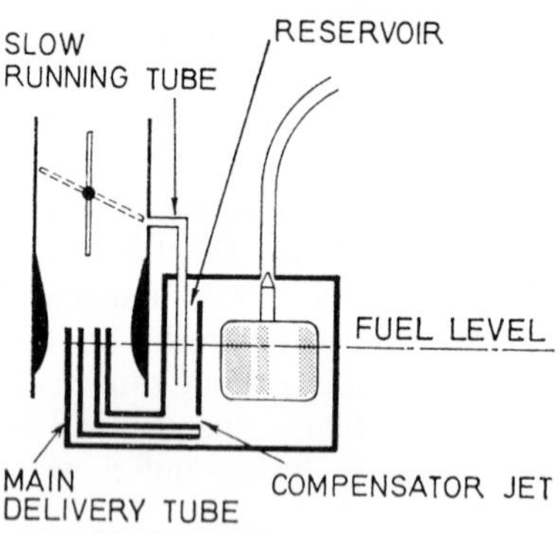

Fig. 35 Compensated carburettor

Fig. 34. At the lower end of the speed range, flow from the compensator jet increases with increase in engine speed up to a point determined by the fact that the compensator jet is located between the float chamber and a reservoir open to atmosphere. Flow from the compensator jet reaches its limit as soon as the reservoir empties. From this point onwards the flow is limited to that caused by the head of fuel in the float chamber. By suitably dividing the flow between the two jets it is possible to get a total flow that gives a reasonably constant mixture strength over the whole speed range of the engine.

Compensation by the two-jet system does not provide satisfactory results for large engines where the consumption is great enough to make errors a matter of some consequence. For these engines the diffuser system shown in Fig. 36 provides a better solution. Fuel is

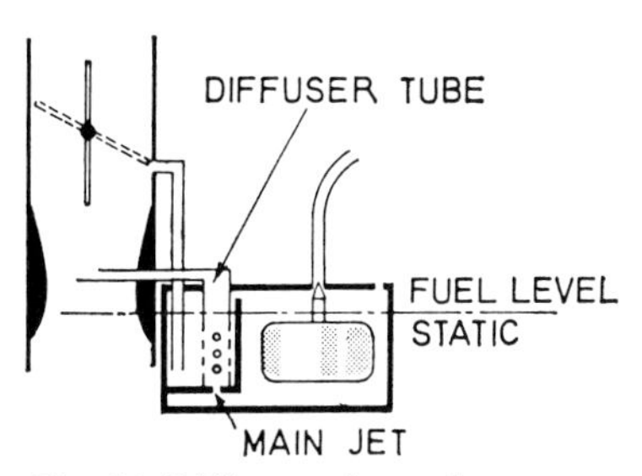

Fig. 36 Diffuser tube carburettor

supplied from the float chamber through the main jet to a perforated tube leading to the delivery in the choke. The perforated tube is contained in a reservoir supplied with fuel that has passed through the main jet. Before the engine is started up, fuel floods the diffuser tube covering all the holes as shown in Fig. 36. When the engine is running the depression in the choke is in communication with the top of the fuel in the diffuser tube and fuel is drawn into the induction system. As the demand for fuel rises the level in the reservoir drops and holes in the diffuser tube are exposed. Atmospheric air entering at these holes reduces the depression applied to the top of the fuel in the diffuser tube to something less than that in the choke and in this way prevents an excess of fuel from being drawn into the engine. As the demand becomes heavier more holes are exposed so that the mixture may be held to any desired strength. The position and size of the holes in the diffuser tube are determined by experiment to give the mixture strengths required at various points throughout the working range of the engine. It is not necessary to hold the mixture strength constant over the whole range if it is found that some peculiarity in the induction system demands a weaker or a richer mixture to give satisfactory running at some particular point in the range.

It is probably clear by now that the choke tube carburettor is by no means as simple as was at first indicated. Further complications may be added to provide a suitable slightly weak mixture for cruising and richer mixtures for acceleration and full power when the demands are particularly heavy.

63. Correction for Altitude

The aircraft carburettor has also to deal with the problem brought about by the reduction of density that takes place in the atmosphere at higher altitudes. All other things being equal an engine swallows the same volume of air per minute at all altitudes, but the weight swallowed becomes less as height increases. Correction for the drop in atmospheric pressure is usually initiated by an *aneroid*, the capsules of which expand as the pressure decreases and bring about the operation of a variable jet or other device to restrict the flow of fuel to an extent sufficient to prevent the mixture from becoming rich.

64. Icing

In the vicinity of the carburettor choke and throttle there are conditions akin to those in the freezing compartment of a refrigerator, brought about as heat is removed by the evaporation of fuel in this area. The drop in temperature that results from this absorption of heat can be enough to freeze the moisture in the air, causing ice to build up in the choke and around the throttle (Fig. 37) to an extent

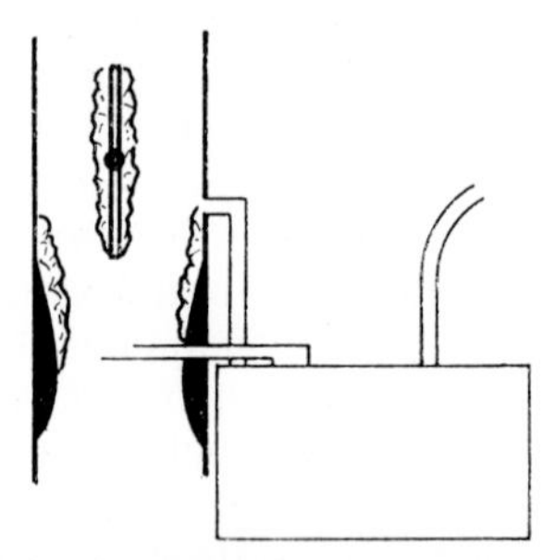

Fig. 37 Ice formation on choke and throttle

that alters the shape of the passage-way and may move the zone of low pressure away from the delivery tube. When this happens the engine stops, and it probably will not restart until heat is conducted along the manifold from the hotter parts of the engine and melts the ice. Alcohol may be added to the fuel to depress the freezing point, but a more certain cure is to supply the throttle and choke with heat by passing hot oil or hot coolant through suitable jackets. If the development of maximum power is a major consideration, the heat applied through these jackets should not be more than is needed to melt the ice or prevent it from forming, otherwise the air density is reduced.

65. Injectors

Quite early in the development of the piston engine it was realized that the choke tube carburettor has fundamental weaknesses when maximum power is of vital importance. To achieve freedom from icing by supplying heat to the intake unfortunately reduces power by reducing the air density, and the presence of the choke places a restriction on the entry of the air. Not least, a simple float chamber will not operate when inverted, or under negative g. These facts were recognized during World War I and an alternative to the carburettor was devised but did not come into widespread use until World War II. This approach to the problem is based on the assumption that the air consumed by the engine is directly proportional to the engine speed. The fuel supply is metered accordingly, with corrections applied for air temperature and pressure.

Some of the principles of this type of fuel injector merit attention because of the insertion of automatic safeguards between the pilot's control lever and the throttle in the induction pipe, even though the arrangement shown dates from 1943 and has not been used for many years (Fig. 38). The pump, which is not shown, is an interesting combination of a vane type pump supplying fuel in excess of requirements at all times, with arrangements to bypass the surplus, and a centrifugal pump to create a pressure difference which is proportional to the speed of rotation. The pressure difference is used to pass the main fuel through a metering orifice with characteristics such that, in conjunction with those of the centrifugal pump, the flow is proportional to the r.p.m. of the engine. The air consumption of the engine also depends on the density of the air, so corrections to fuel flow must be made to allow for changes in manifold temperatures and pressures.

The main metering valve on which corrections are applied consists of an inner sleeve and two outer sleeves, one of which is fixed and the other positioned according to the temperature in the manifold. The inner sleeve has a port cut in it which is approximately triangular in shape with the apex at the top. The effective size of the port depends on the space between the two outer sleeves and on the position of the inner sleeve. The inner sleeve is connected to an aneroid acted on by manifold pressure. High pressures contract the aneroid and raise the inner sleeve to increase the port size and give a bigger fuel flow to match the higher air density, while low manifold pressures have the reverse effect. The outer sleeve is actuated by a Bourdon tube which deflects with changes of temperature in such a way as to close the gap between the sleeves when the temperature is high and open it when the temperature is low.

The engine power is regulated by a throttle plate in much the usual way but in this case there is no direct connection between the pilot's control lever and the throttle plate. The mechanism is shown in Fig. 38 and its action may best be understood by following the sequence of

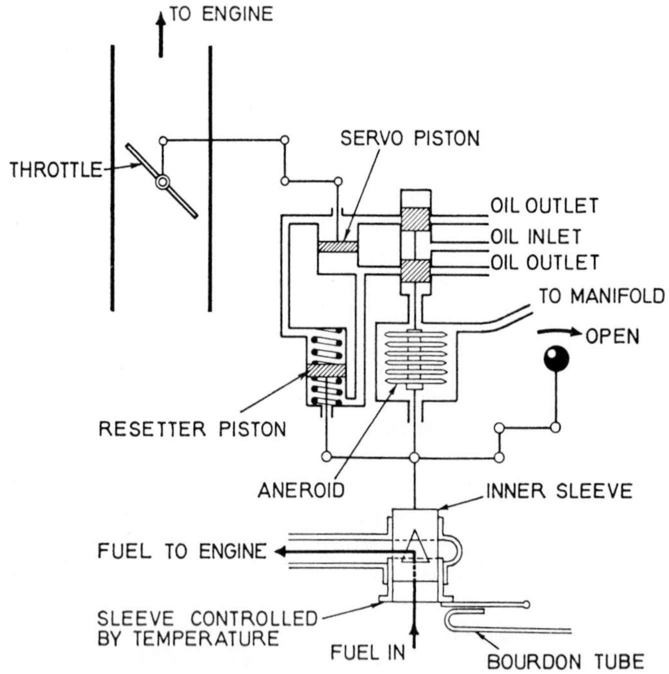

Fig. 38 Throttle mechanism of injector

events that results from movements of the control lever. If the engine is running steadily at part throttle, when the control lever (black ball) is moved forward to call for more power the aneroid is raised bodily and with it the valve controlling oil flow to and from the servo piston. High-pressure oil is directed to the top of the servo piston and the throttle is moved towards the open position; the main metering valve is also opened to give the required increase in the flow of fuel. With the opening of the throttle the manifold pressure rises and the aneroid contracts to cut off oil flow to the servo piston. The system now settles down to a stable condition until once more required to respond to changes of pressure, temperature or pilot's control position.

When the aircraft climbs above full throttle height (see Section 87), the manifold pressure decreases and causes expansion of the aneroid and opens the oil control valve. As the servo piston is already at the end of its travel at full throttle height no further motion can take place and the pressure builds up until it overcomes the spring in the resetter piston chamber. Downward movement of the resetter piston causes partial closure of the main metering valve and reduces fuel flow to suit the decreased density of the air entering the engine. This system is suitable for large engines operating over a wide range and in conditions that justify the degree of complication involved. A much simpler system for smaller engines is shown in block diagram form in Fig. 39.

The pump of this simpler injector system is of the positive displacement vane type capable of delivering rather more fuel than the engine can possibly consume. The excess fuel is returned to the pump inlet through an orifice and spring-loaded relief valve which together maintain a pump pressure and delivery proportional to engine speed. The air supply is controlled by a throttle in the usual way, and a fuel control is linked to the throttle so as to move a cam-shaped disc over the delivery port in order to regulate the orifice size to suit the throttle position. A manually operated mixture-control valve is assembled in the same bore as the fuel-control valve and gives the option of full rich, part lean, and idle cut-off settings.

From the fuel control assembly the fuel goes to a manifold valve for distribution to the individual nozzles at each cylinder. A spring-loaded diaphragm controls a plunger in the central bore which cuts off the supply of fuel to the cylinders when the pressure in the fuel line drops below a predetermined value as would happen with the closing of the idle cut-off. The fuel discharge nozzles are located in the cylinder heads and direct the spray into the inlet ports. As the fuel passes through the nozzles air is picked up and thoroughly mixed with it to assist the process of atomization.

The flat-six Continental engine shown in Plate 4 is fitted with this rather inconspicuous injection system. The petrol pump is on the front cover at the underside close to the flexible mounting. It is possible to trace the fuel pipe from the pump to the control unit mounted near the Y-junction in the induction manifold. Another flexible pipe leads to the fuel manifold valve on the top of the engine, with branch pipes to each cylinder. Only one nozzle is visible in the picture, entering at the underside of the inlet port on the first cylinder on the left bank in the photograph.

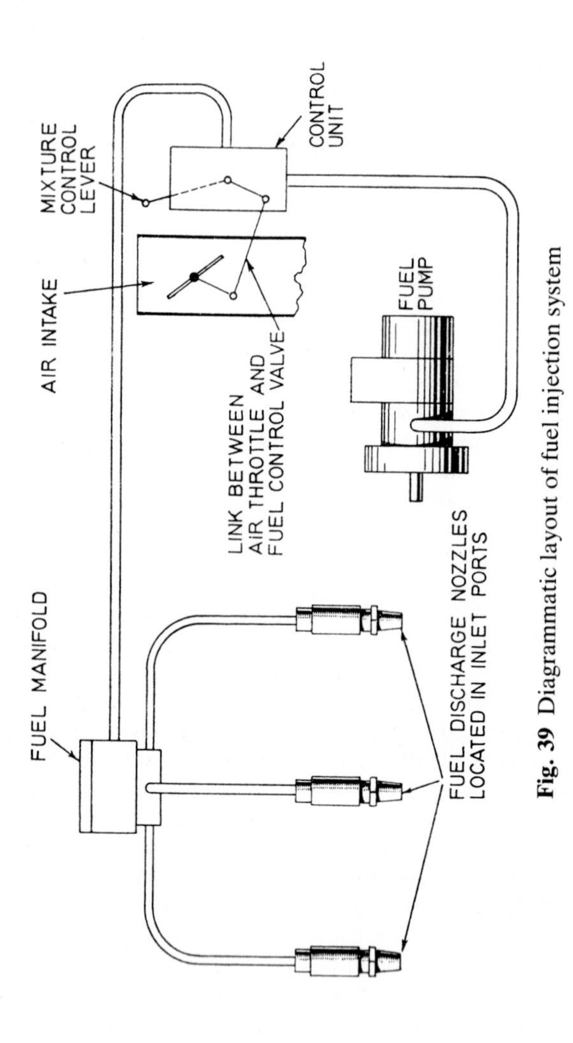

Fig. 39 Diagrammatic layout of fuel injection system

One great benefit of any injector system is that each cylinder stands a very good chance of getting a fair share of the fuel, without the risk of certain constituents being carried along to a few favoured cylinders as was mentioned in Section 55. Better distribution means more power, because poor distribution leaves some of the cylinders short of fuel and possibly of tetraethyl lead. Injection also removes the risk of icing by delivering the fuel directly to a reasonably hot zone – right into the inlet port or into the eye of the supercharger.

66. Supplying the Fuel to the Gas Turbine

Compared with the variety of gadgets needed to get the fuel into the piston engine cylinders, the equipment used on the turbine appears to be very simple, as indeed it is until closer attention is paid to the question of controlling the fuel flow to suit requirements. It will then be realized that there are very good reasons for introducing fuel systems very briefly at this stage and leaving the finer details of control until later.

Some of the simplest gas turbines use fuel pumps little changed from 40 years ago. One type of pump delivers fuel at a steady rate, any excess over that needed by the engine being bypassed back to the pump inlet. The other (Fig. 40) controls the fuel delivery and only pumps as much fuel as the engine requires at any instant. The pump rotor carries a number of spring-loaded plungers which are spaced round the spindle and bear on a tilted cam plate. As the shaft rotates, the plungers are forced to oscillate in the rotor body, drawing in fuel through one port and delivering it through another. The tilt of the cam plate can be varied from a position at right-angles to the axis when the delivery is nil to a position like the one shown which gives maximum plunger stroke and maximum delivery. The position of the cam plate is fixed by a servo piston, one side of which is connected to the high-pressure fuel line and the other loaded by a spring to move the cam plate to the maximum delivery position whenever pressure permits. The spring side of the piston is connected to a number of valves and to the left-hand side of the piston, in the position drawn, through a restrictor valve. When all the valves are closed the pressure equalizes on the two sides of the piston and the spring pushes the piston along so that the cam plate is held in the maximum delivery position. If, for any reason, one of the valves connected to the right-hand side of the piston is opened, the pressure on that side is relieved and the piston moves to the right, placing the cam plate so that the pump delivers something less than the maximum amount of fuel. The valves are connected to a variety of sensing devices which observe jet

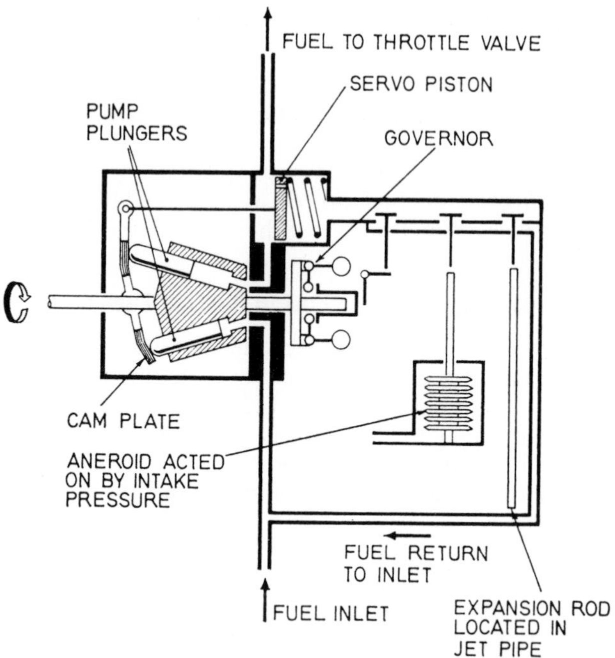

Fig. 40 Variable-stroke pump with override controls for speed, pressure and temperature

pipe temperature, compressor pressure, speed (centrifugal flyweight governor) or any other relevant function, and cause the valves to open if any of the values exceed certain limits.

67. Combustion in the Gas Turbine

One of the attractive features of the gas turbine is the enormous power that can be developed by engines which are of modest size and weight considering the work they can do. The vast amount of energy involved can only be released by burning considerable quantities of fuel and air under carefully controlled conditions, but the temperature that exists in the flame from a burning hydrocarbon fuel is too high to be in contact with the materials that are available. Fortunately jet propulsion and the gas turbine are based on the use of four or five times as much air as is needed to burn the fuel, and this excess air is used to shield the metal from the flames. The air and the products of combustion must be thoroughly mixed as soon as possible so that there are no extra-hot zones in the gas by the time it reaches the turbine.

68. Burners and Combustion Chambers

There are two main types of burner in use: the atomizer type in which the fuel is introduced as a very fine spray, and the vaporizer type in which the heat of combustion is used to vaporize the fuel before it reaches the combustion zone. Each of these burner types may be used in a variety of combustion chamber arrangements that has grown up as techniques and knowledge have improved.

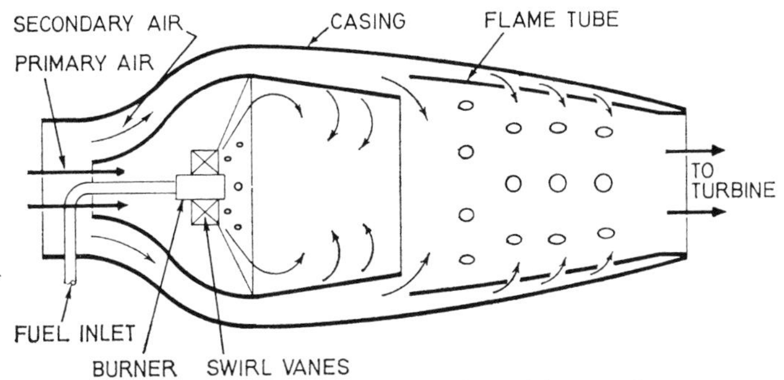

Fig. 41 Individual combustion chamber with spray burner

The earliest combustion systems were developed as a number of separate chambers arranged in parallel and grouped round the main-shaft. These separate chambers, which are shown in Fig. 41 and Plate 23, allowed freedom for experimental work on single chambers and for the replacement of faulty units without major dismantling.

As combustion chambers became more reliable, the flame tubes were spaced round an annulus to give an arrangement that is slightly more compact and in which the sheet metal work is simpler but the individual flame tubes are not at all accessible.

A further development replaced the group of individual flame tubes by a single annular part to obtain a combustion chamber which made the greatest possible use of the space inside the casing. Success with this type of chamber has come with the development of durable alloys and better ways of manufacturing them, which combine to give the chambers long life and very satisfactory performance.

All three combustion chamber types are based on principles which vary only in detail. In each case the total airflow from the compressor is divided on reaching the combustion chambers so that the primary supply which enters the combustion zone and mixes with the fuel gives an approximately correct mixture. The secondary air is fed in at several points along the flame tubes to mix with the hot burning gases and bring the temperature down to some value, depending on the engine, at which the high-pressure turbine rotor blades will unfailingly reach their design operating life of several thousand hours.

The paths chosen for the airflow are such as to ensure that the light sheet metal is always shielded from the hottest gases by a film of colder air. On its way into the flame tube the primary air passes over twisted vanes which set it whirling vigorously, so that it fans out under the action of centrifugal force to follow the domed end of the chamber and protect it from the flame. The whirling of the air also creates a zone of low pressure at the centre and coaxes the air to double back into the area where burning is taking place. This region of stalled airflow allows the flame to be established without risk of being blown out by the main blast which travels at a speed which is high enough to whip the flame away from the burners. This same principle is also used in ramjets and in jet pipes when running with reheat. Fuel is injected into the stalled area, either as a vapour or as an exceedingly fine spray, to mix with the air so as to give very rapid burning in the shortest possible length of chamber. The secondary air may be introduced simply to dilute and cool the gases or it may be used to promote more turbulence and supply more oxygen if combustion is still going on at that point. It is vitally important that mixing should be sufficiently thorough to ensure an even distribution of heat throughout the gases so that the blades of the turbine are not exposed to hot tongues of flame.

Burners and combustion chambers have been developed to a state of high efficiency which ensures the release of large quantities of heat with remarkably few thermal or other losses. The fabrication of the chambers has raised the sheet metal workers' art to something very close to precision engineering.

69. Power, Power Limitations and Power Boosting

With the exception of the introductory sections on propellers and propulsion, we have been concerned so far with a study of what has to be done to get the fuel and air into a suitable condition and ready to burn in the engine. The effort that goes into preparing the working substance for action may be regarded as something of an uphill task, particularly in the turbine, with the ever-present risk that one false move will lead to the loss of vast quantities of energy with no useful work to show for it. This can happen when surge interferes with the normal working of a rotary compressor.

The expansion process, on the other hand, is on a downhill course and the gases have no inherent objection to moving in the desired direction. It now remains to be seen how the energy given to the air by compression and by burning fuel is harnessed to do a useful job, how this can be done efficiently, and how the power may be boosted if required.

Power generation during expansion in the piston engine has very little in common with what happens at the corresponding stage in the turbine. Separate treatment of the two engine types again becomes necessary except for a brief mention of horse-power.

70. Transmission Dynamometers

The terms brake horse-power and shaft horse-power used in piston engine and turbine practice respectively refer to precisely the same thing – how much work can be done per minute by the engine. The term brake horse-power came into general use at a time when it was necessary to absorb the power developed (and get rid of it as heat) so as to measure it. Wasteful perhaps, but the only way then known of finding out what an engine could do, and essential when making comparisons after adjustments or changes in design. In certain marine applications it became possible to assess engine performance at sea by measuring, electrically, the twist in the propeller shaft whilst transmitting power. Subsequently the use of another form of transmission dynamometer or torquemeter came into use in aircraft engines when the adoption of constant-speed propellers took much of the significance out of r.p.m. as an indication of performance. When fixed-pitch propellers are in use the engine speed is a fair indication of power since the resistance of the propeller must be overcome to achieve the speed, but with the constant-speed propeller the picture is quite different. Any tendency for the speed to fluctuate results in a change of pitch to restore r.p.m. irrespective of the power. A serious loss of power may make itself felt in other ways, but in a multi-engined aircraft one engine might get away with less than its full share of the work because a finer propeller pitch enabled it to maintain r.p.m.

Most aircraft dynamometers take advantage of the fact that the reduction gears are epicyclic, and as such must have a gear ring which has to be restrained from turning whilst power is being transmitted. In the gear shown in Fig. 42 power enters at *A* and causes rotation of wheels *B* within the annulus *C*. As wheels *B* rotate and make their

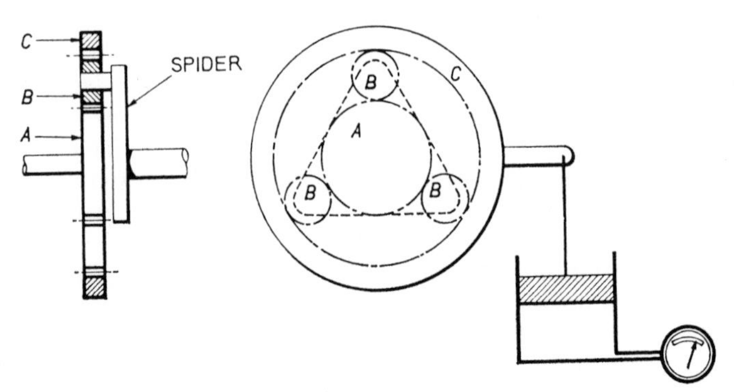

Fig. 42 Transmission dynamometer or torquemeter

way round inside *C*, the spider on which they are mounted is forced to turn about the same axis as *A*. If *C* were not restrained the spider would almost certainly stand still and the annulus would spin idly round. When this system is used in aircraft engines the restraint is provided by hydraulic plungers, and the pressure built up behind these plungers is proportional to the torque transmitted. Taken in conjunction with the r.p.m. and certain dimensions of the dynamometer, sufficient information is available to enable horse-power to be calculated. There is no need to do these calculations under normal flying conditions as satisfactory readings of torquemeter pressure and r.p.m. indicate that all is well.

71. Radial and In-line Piston Engines

The power developed by any piston engine must depend on many things – the pressure in the cylinders, the dimensions of the cylinders, and how many power strokes there are per minute (and this in turn depends on the number of cylinders, the r.p.m., and on whether the engine is working on the two-stroke cycle or the four). Obviously the designer has a lot to think about in the early stages. Whether to go for a small number of large cylinders in a slow-speed engine (necessarily so because of the inertia forces set up by the heavy pistons) or whether to go for a larger number of smaller cylinders in an engine capable of running at a higher speed, is but one of the major problems that confront him. The existence of jigs, tools and even serviceable components may dictate the choice of dimensions, for although this may not give the designer a completely free hand, there is comfort in the knowledge provided by experience. Parts which have proved satisfactory in the past will probably do so again if not overloaded; even the troublesome parts will have shown where improvements are needed.

The problem of removing heat from the exhaust valve head and from the piston crown usually puts a limit to the size of cylinder and to the power that can be extracted from it. If this limit is accepted, as obviously it must be when there are facts to work on, the only variable factor left may be the number of cylinders. Today almost all engines have two, three, four or six cylinders, though in Poland radial engines with seven or nine cylinders are still made in small numbers.

Aircraft engines are grouped in two main types according to the cylinder arrangement adopted. The radial engines have the cylinders arranged like the spokes of a wheel in a plane at right-angles to the crankshaft, whilst the in-line have theirs in rows or banks with the cylinders in the same plane as the crankshaft.

The radial engines may have 5, 7, or 9 cylinders with connecting rods sharing a single-throw crank, or twice as many in two rows with a two-throw crank; the odd number of cylinders is needed to give even firing intervals. Figure 18 has been put together to show the activities in each of the five cylinders of a small radial engine and from this it may be seen that the firing order is 1, 3, 5, 2, 4. Although the firing intervals are equal this does not guarantee a smooth-running engine. A very complex system of forces arises from the acceleration and retardation applied to the pistons and this cannot be completely balanced out by the crankshaft counterweights. The magnitude of the out-of-balance forces may not be serious but vibration can be set up and transmitted to the airframe.

The radial layout is a particularly good one for an air-cooled engine as all the cylinders are presented equally to the airflow. As the induction system is symmetrical with all the inlet ports at the same distance from the supercharger, distribution is good. As all the cylinders of one bank drive on to a single crankpin the radial type of engine is inherently compact. On the other hand it tends to have a large frontal area.

Today's piston engines can be loosely divided into those for microlights and related small aircraft, and those for larger aircraft of a traditional nature. For the latter market the four-stroke with horizontally opposed cylinders reigns supreme except for the specialized aerobatic category where the dominant engine is a Polish (Soviet designed) 360-h.p. radial. Until 1980 air-cooled cylinders were universal, but today liquid cooling is fast gaining ground. Indeed, in the microlight category the choice is even wider, because mass-produced engines have air or liquid cooling and work on either the four- or two-stroke cycle.

Many microlight engines have only one or two cylinders (Plates 2 and 3). In larger sizes this would result in very rough running, with severe vibration, but this is less of a problem with small engines running at high speeds, such as 9,000 r.p.m. In recent years unconventional engines have also become important, as explained in the extra text added at the back of this edition.

Any study of aviation piston engines will indicate the diversity of layouts that has grown up, each with its own merits and none with appreciably more than another. Fortunately the various designs are a source of interest rather than a problem to us, as our concern is with what goes on inside the cylinders, irrespective of layouts and dimensions, so that we can follow the trends and understand the limitations.

The power developed in an engine depends on the weight of air that can be drawn into the cylinders per minute and this in turn depends on a number of design features and running conditions. Anything which obstructs the airflow into the cylinders or reduces the air density by heating has an adverse effect on power. Air filter, choke, throttle, rough surfaces and badly matched joints all contribute to the total resistance to the ingoing charge. Some of these ill effects may be reduced by design as, for example, by arranging for the throttle to retract completely when full power is required or by adopting an injection system that needs no choke. Most of the losses increase in severity as the engine speed is increased, so for this reason it pays to keep down the r.p.m. and run with the throttle wide open. The effect of reduced atmospheric density has already been mentioned in Section 35 together with the cure – supercharging.

Since supercharging is effective in restoring power at altitude it is perfectly natural to wonder why it is not used to boost the power of the engine at sea-level to a greater extent than is done at present. The answer is tied up with detonation, strength of materials and cooling. Increasing the supercharger pressure is bound to increase the risk of detonation, but assuming this is overcome somehow (with a super fuel, for example) we are next up against the problem of increased stresses in the engine parts; these would have to be strengthened, with increase in weight. The cooling problem is a serious one because the real danger spots – exhaust valves and piston crowns – are hard to reach with the coolant. This point alone will often dictate that engine size can only be increased by adding more cylinders.

In fact, for 40 years nobody has wanted to add cylinders or increase the size of piston engines. Except for the special fields of agricultural spraying/dusting aircraft and fire bombers, few piston engines are in use with takeoff power greater than 360 h.p. For all higher powers the gas turbine reigns supreme, and in the following sections we look at the gas turbine itself, which extracts the power from the white-hot gas.

72. Expansion in the Gas Turbine

Expansion in the gas turbine looks just like letting the high-pressure gases escape to atmosphere, and that is indeed all that happens. However, in the process heat is converted to kinetic energy, and the velocity change that takes place as the hot gases pass through the turbine results in the application of force to the blades and torque to the turbine shaft. The gas continues to expand and increase its kinetic energy as it passes through the propulsion nozzle, and it is the increase in gas velocity in its passage through the engine that determines the thrust of the turbojet.

73. Turbines

The turbine wheel offers a compact means of converting gas energy into shaft work in a manner which seems straightforward at first but gets more and more complicated as it is studied in detail. However, taking a little at a time and focusing attention on one point at a time it may be possible to gain a useful grasp of the subject.

In turbojets the turbine extracts sufficient energy to drive the compressor and auxiliaries, leaving the remainder of the energy to provide propulsive thrust. When a propeller is used, more energy is extracted at the turbine and less remains available to give propulsive thrust at the jet pipe. The number of turbine wheels varies according to engine type; a small turbojet may need only one, while the GE90, a particularly large turbofan, has a two-stage HP turbine driving the compressor and a seven-stage LP turbine driving the fan.

The conversion of heat to kinetic energy downstream of the turbines depends on the pressure drop available. As this in turn depends on the extent to which the pressure rise, given partly by ram and partly in the compressor, is reduced by driving the turbines, it is not very great considering how much heat is available. This low expansion ratio is inherently inefficient and much of the heat cannot be recovered by conversion to kinetic energy. Attempts have been made to recover some of the heat by means of heat exchangers, but although these have had a measure of success in land installations the bulk, weight and cost are against their use in aircraft. This matter of increasing the engine weight in the search for fuel economy is an important one as the aircraft may have to fly a very long way before the savings in weight and cost justify the heavier powerplant. In this context it must be remembered that any extra weight of metal in the engine is always there, whereas the weight of the remaining fuel, and hence the total weight of the aircraft, becomes steadily less as the flight progresses.

When considering what the gases have to do it is as well to realize that the word turbine covers also the static nozzle ring that lies ahead of the moving blades. This ring fulfils the twofold task of whirling the gas in the direction of rotation and increasing its velocity if the turbine happens to be one that requires this to be done. Two distinct turbine types are recognized, the impulse turbine and the reaction turbine, although few if any large turbines belong solely to either type. In many turbines the best compromise is obtained with blades in which part is in one category and the rest of the blade in the other.

The *impulse turbine* is designed to give the whole of the pressure drop, and therefore the whole velocity increase, in the nozzles. To achieve this the passages formed by the nozzle blades are convergent so that the gases have to go faster to get through the narrowing gap. The width of the passages formed by the rotor blades is constant, and the gas passes through without change in speed or pressure, but it does change direction. The blades must apply force to the gas to make it change direction and it is the reaction to this force which makes the wheel rotate. Pure impulse blading does not appear on the turbines of large engines but may be seen in some gas starters and in the turbines used to harness the exhaust energy in piston engines. In this latter application it is important that the turbines do not set up undue back pressure, as that would offset any gain by reducing the power of the piston engine because of the work to be done in overcoming the extra resistance during the exhaust stroke.

The *reaction turbine* is one in which the whole of the pressure drop and the velocity increase occur as the gas flows through the rotor blade passages. The nozzle passages are of constant width and curved or angled to give the gases whirl in the direction in which the wheel rotates. There are probably no commercial examples of this type of turbine although the principle is used in sundry demonstrations of the Hero turbine.

Practical turbines are a compromise and in those of the impulse-reaction type the gas passages converge all the way from the nozzle entry to the rotor outlet. By sharing the gas acceleration between both components of the turbine the risk of encountering more extreme conditions in one part than in the other is minimized.

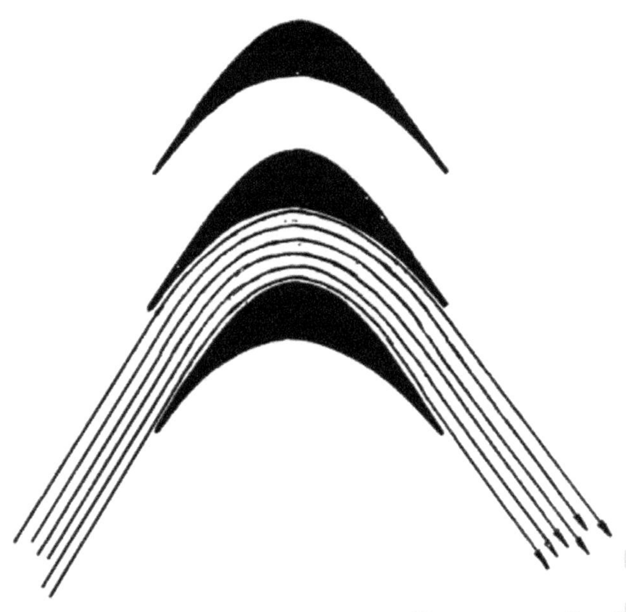

Figure 5: Impulse turbine moving blades

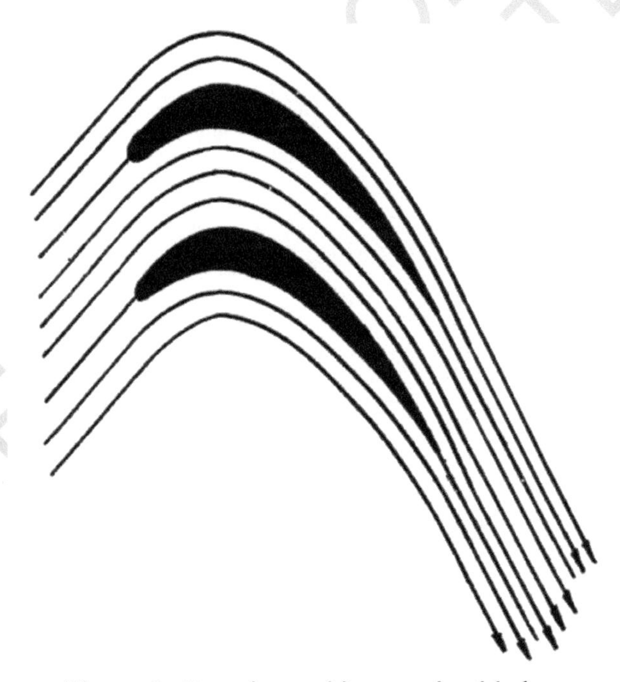

Figure 6: Reaction turbine moving blades

74. Effect of Free Vortex Flow on Blade Shape

Whilst it is possible to design for impulse-reaction conditions at a special station along the length of the blade, usually at the mean height, the existence of free vortex flow distorts the state of affairs to a greater or lesser degree at all other stations. As in the axial compressor the effect of free vortex flow is probably best demonstrated by the comparison of simple velocity diagrams for various stations along the length of a typical blade.

For a simple turbojet the nozzle and turbine blades may look something like those shown in Fig. 43 at the blade mean height. In

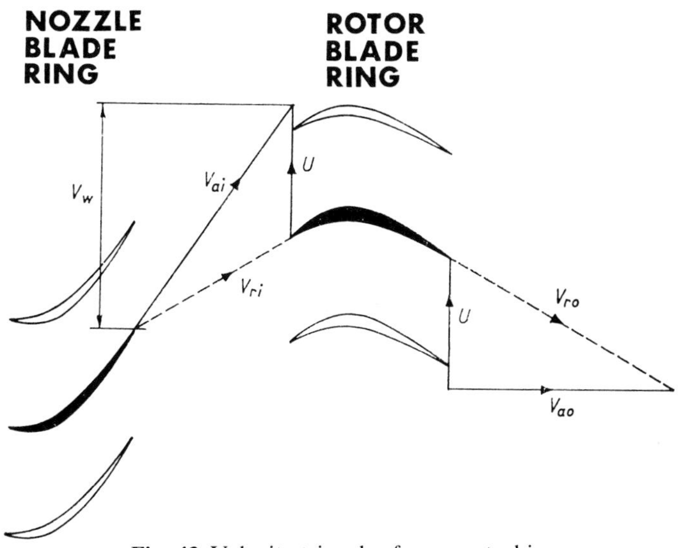

Fig. 43 Velocity triangles for a gas turbine

V_{ai} is the absolute gas velocity at the rotor blade inlet
V_{ri} is the relative gas velocity at the rotor blade inlet
U is the blade velocity
V_{ao} is the absolute gas velocity at the rotor blade outlet
V_{ro} is the relative gas velocity at the rotor blade outlet
V_w is the whirl velocity given to the gas in the nozzle ring; the rotational energy is entirely used up in driving the turbine

the nozzle passages the gas accelerates as the pressure drops and the set of the blades is such as to whirl the gases in the direction of the blade movement. The whirl energy given to the gases should be sufficient to drive the compressor but only just, as any residual whirl energy would not contribute to the thrust. The whirl imparted has the additional advantage that it reduces the relative velocity of the gas at the entry to the rotor. Complete absence of whirl in the jet pipe is probably only possible at one running condition, and over much of the range there will be some whirl in the gas as it leaves the jet pipe.

As in the case of the axial compressor, once the gas has been given whirl the flow becomes free vortex unless forced to adopt some other pattern. This can influence blade shape as shown in Fig. 44. There are no mysteries about the velocities on which these diagrams are based, they are easily calculable, reasonably representative and serve to illustrate some important points. In Section 47 it was stated that the velocity of whirl is a maximum at the root and decreases towards the tip, whereas the blade speed increases from root to tip. These opposing tendencies change the shape of the velocity diagrams from the symmetrical one that applies at mean height. Notice that at the root the gas is turned through a much sharper angle than at the other two stations and that there is little or no change in gas velocity between blade inlet and blade outlet. These are the conditions already defined as impulse earlier in Section 73. Relative velocity is also highest at the root and therefore it is in this vicinity that the gas will first reach the speed of sound relative to the blade if it is going to do so at all. Should this happen choking will occur, that is, the gas will reach a limiting velocity beyond which it cannot be pushed by increase in pressure alone. Any attempt to get more power by admitting more fuel to the combustion chambers might just increase the pressure at that point, check the flow of air from the compressor, and finally cause stalling followed by surge unless in the meantime fuel flow had been reduced to allow the pressures in the combustion chambers to return to normal.

Conditions at the mean height give the desirable impulse-reaction state in which the change in absolute velocity is equal, numerically, to the change in relative velocity.

At the tip there is very little gas acceleration in the nozzles and a considerable amount in the rotor channels, indicating the existence of reaction conditions. Therefore over the length of the blade there has been a complete change from impulse to reaction type. Other conditions of flow may be imposed to meet special requirements but the ones described serve to indicate the range possible in any one blade.

When shaft power is more important than jet thrust and more energy has to be extracted at the turbine, it is advisable to share the pressure drop involved over several stages. Nozzle rings are placed between each row of rotor blades to whirl the gas in the appropriate direction and direct it into subsequent rotor rings. Each successive stage has longer blades than the previous one and the annulus

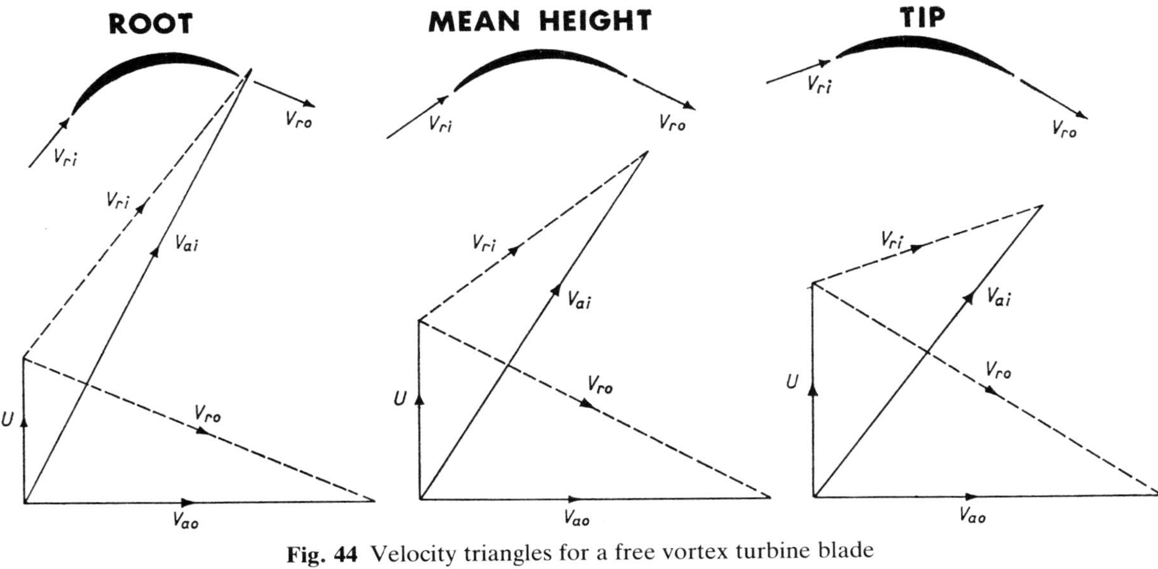

Fig. 44 Velocity triangles for a free vortex turbine blade

Symbols

V_{ai} is the absolute gas velocity at the rotor inlet
V_{ri} is the relative gas velocity at the rotor inlet
V_{ao} is the absolute gas velocity at the rotor outlet
U is the blade speed, increasing from root to tip
V_{ro} is the relative gas velocity at the rotor outlet

increases in size towards the rear to allow for the fact that the gases are expanding as they move downstream (Fig. 53).

75. Limiting Conditions at the Turbine

No component in the whole engine has to operate under more exacting conditions than those to which the turbine blades are subjected. In addition to the very high temperatures at which they have to work the blades are heavily loaded by centrifugal force and by the pressure of the gases. As both maximum power and efficiency depend on a high temperature at the turbine entry, no efforts are spared to make advances in metallurgy and in manufacturing techniques that will permit even higher temperatures to be used. The higher temperatures are easily obtained, if there is an opportunity to use them, as the maximum temperature in the combustion zone is at least twice what the normal blades could be expected to stand. It is the blades which are the bottleneck. Metallurgists have gone a long way towards solving the problem by producing alloys which are of great strength at high temperatures (and at the same time have set some ticklish jobs in shaping their excellent metals to the form of turbine blades!). Alongside this development many ideas have been followed up in an effort to cool the blades, for from the performance point of view there is no reason at all why the blades should be as hot as the gases. An indirect form of cooling has always been provided by a blast of air on the blade drum, which carries away heat transferred to the drum from the blades by conduction through the roots, and now there is also direct cooling by a current of air blown through passages formed in the blades.

Today's high-pressure turbine blades are fantastic technological achievements. For a start they are made in alloys deliberately selected to retain strength at almost white heat, so they are clearly difficult to shape! Second, their interiors are as complex as the London underground, with dozens of paths for cooling air and numerous microscopic holes where the air enters and leaves, the air expelled under high pressure forming a thin protective skin surrounding the metal. Third, even the raw material is no longer merely forged or cast. Some blades are of DS (directionally solidified) type, in which all the microscopic crystals of the alloy are preferentially aligned to give maximum strength along the blade's length, where stress is greatest, in the same way that a joiner chooses the direction of a wood grain for maximum strength. The most advanced blades, used in all the latest jetliners, are of the SC (single-crystal) type, in which weak inter-crystal boundaries are eliminated (Plate 24).

76. Radial-Flow Turbines

The first jet aeroplane, the Heinkel He 178, had a crude turbojet with a radial-flow turbine. This operates like a centrifugal compressor in reverse (Fig. 45). Such turbines are seen in a handful of tiny turbojets

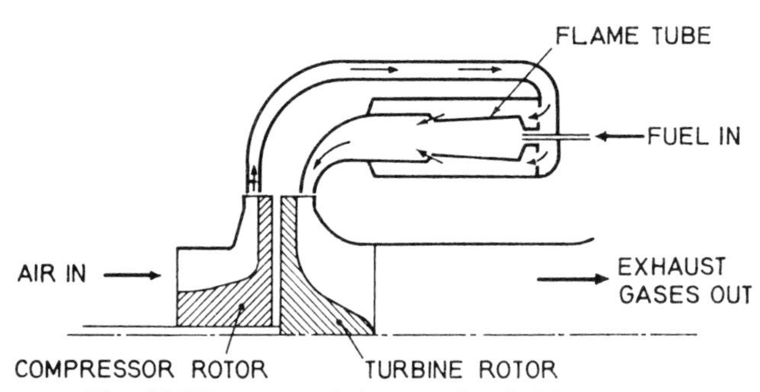

Fig. 45 Diagrammatic layout of radial-flow turbine

and auxiliary units. Of course the turbine must be made of heat-resisting material. Nozzles take the place of diffuser vanes and hot gases are fed inwards through them to impinge on the rotor blades. In addition to the force applied directly in this way there is a reaction on the blades when the gases leave near the hub. Mounting the turbine and compressor rotors back to back gives a very compact arrangement with a bit of heat sharing that is good for the turbine but not for compressor efficiency. Efficiency is limited because of the modest pressure ratio obtainable with the centrifugal compressor, but as the maximum power is not great and running is for short periods only, heavy fuel consumption is not likely to be a problem.

77. Jet Pipes

In its simplest form the jet pipe is used to conduct the exhaust gases from the turbine outlet to the point chosen for release to the atmosphere. When the turbojet is mounted in a pod or nacelle, the outlet may be annular and the pipe itself very short, giving an arrangement in which losses are small.

If the engine is mounted in the fuselage or buried in the wing, a longer jet pipe is needed and it is usual to change the cross-section from annular at the turbine outlet to circular at the tip of the exhaust cone. The exhaust cone also shields the turbine disc from the hot gases which would otherwise eddy into the space behind the disc and cause overheating. There is nothing very vital about the jet pipe diameter downstream of the exhaust cone and some increase in diameter reduces the gas velocity and so minimizes frictional losses. At the outlet the diameter is reduced so as to give the maximum possible velocity as the gas expands to atmospheric pressure. The highest possible velocity obtainable with a convergent nozzle is the speed of sound appropriate to the temperature of the gas. The highest thrust is obtained most economically when the issuing gas just reaches the speed of sound and atmospheric pressure at the jet pipe outlet. If the pressure is any higher there is an element of pressure thrust, equal to the product of the outlet area and the pressure difference inside and outside the outlet. When the gases emerge at something more than atmospheric pressure they tend to flare out and eddy with more loss than would occur with smooth acceleration in a substantially axial direction.

A suitable divergent portion on the end of the jet pipe can control the expansion and give additional thrust by enabling the gases to reach supersonic speeds. Such a nozzle is only suited to the case when the gases are at the speed of sound at the narrowest part of the outlet and at a pressure above that of the atmosphere. For other running conditions the divergent part of the nozzle may only be a source of drag, so it is necessary to think in terms of jet pipe outlets that can be varied to match the requirements. More details about this are given in the next two sections.

78. Afterburning (reheat)

Whereas a piston engine normally burns a stoichiometric (ideal) fuel/air mixture, so that in theory there is no unburned oxygen left in the exhaust, the gas turbine invariably has an enormous excess of air over that required to burn the fuel. Most of this air is added around the combustion chamber to cool the metal parts of the combustor, nozzle guide vanes and high-pressure turbine. As a result the propulsive jet contains a high proportion of unburned oxygen, even in a turbojet; in a modern turbofan, with the bypass air mixed with the core jet, the final jet is chemically very much like atmospheric air. Thus there is ample scope for burning additional fuel in the jetpipe downstream of the turbine.

As this afterburning takes place downstream of the turbine there is little need to worry about the temperature reached, and 2,000°C can be permitted in some engines. To reach such a temperature the fuel flow has to be enormous, and afterburning, or reheat, would never be considered except in supersonic aircraft (though it was used in some early subsonic fighters). To propel a highly supersonic aircraft an extremely high jet velocity is needed, and afterburning is used in conjunction with a convergent/divergent nozzle (Fig. 48) in order to accelerate the jet to a high supersonic speed. Shockwaves from the nozzle are repeatedly reflected within the jet, giving rise to bright golden 'shock diamonds'.

The reheat fuel is often fed by a separate turbine-driven pump to several spray rings downstream of the turbine. Immediately downstream of each ring is a flameholder ring with a cross-section like a V or U with the open part facing to the rear (Plate 15). This causes turbulence which slows the gas flow and keeps the flame from being blown out of the jetpipe. With a modern turbofan fighter engine afterburning can boost thrust by almost 100 per cent, but there are drawbacks. Noise is deafening, which rules out this method of thrust boosting for civil use. Infra-red emission is greatly magnified, which makes it undesirable for military use. The Lockheed F-22, the latest USAF fighter, is designed to cruise at about Mach 2 without using afterburning, though it can light reheat fuel if necessary (Plate 19).

79. Adjustable Jet Pipe Nozzles

The gas velocity at a choked jet pipe outlet may be increased in two ways: by burning more fuel in the jet pipe and so raising the local speed of sound, or by providing a divergent nozzle. Neither expedient is easy to apply because what is suitable for one condition of running is likely to prove most unsuitable for another part of the range.

If the case is considered of a turbojet which is developing high thrust, it is almost certain that the gas will be travelling at the speed of sound when it reaches the jet pipe outlet. The burning of extra fuel in the jet pipe will give a small increase in velocity because of the temperature rise, but it is highly probable that the pressure will also rise. This increase in pressure could make itself felt right back to the compressor and could easily cause stalling. Apart from this vital consideration, an increase in pressure inside the jet pipe increases the downstream load (or drag) acting on the inside of the convergent portion of the nozzle (Fig. 46). The real solution is to provide a bigger nozzle so that the gases can escape at the higher velocity without any build-up in pressure to upset the running of the engine or increase the drag at the nozzle. Opening up the nozzle reduces the area on which the pressure is applied so that at the original pressure the drag on the jet pipe is reduced.

Downstream of any afterburner the nozzle has to be fully variable in both area and profile. Indeed, all turbojet or turbofan engines

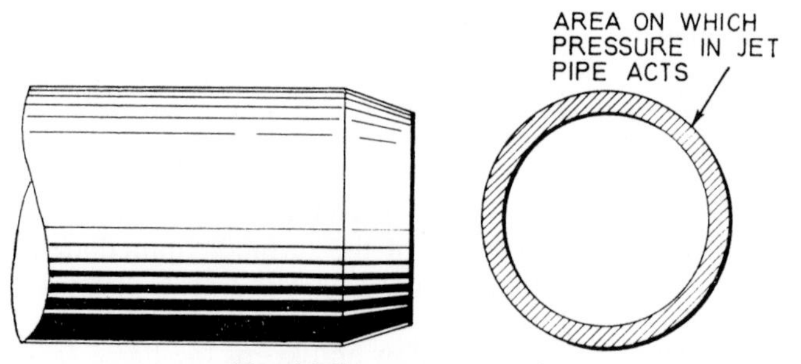

Fig. 46 Convergent nozzle

ought ideally to have variable nozzles, because a jet pipe of fixed area and profile (for example, matched to sea-level takeoff) would give less than the ideal thrust at any other engine operating condition.

The first kind of variable nozzle to be used was the bullet, used in German and French engines prior to 1950. Next came the clamshell, in which the nozzle contains two pivoted parts which can hinge apart to give two profiles and areas. Today nozzles are much more sophisticated, with multiple petals or flaps giving perfect control of an inner primary nozzle and a larger secondary nozzle downstream.

The divergent nozzle which was introduced but not explained in Section 77 must present something of a puzzle when met with for the first time. So far, divergent passages have been regarded as places in which speed is reduced to give increases in pressure, but in this application the divergent duct is actually being used to give an increase in velocity. The difference lies in the speed at which the gas enters the small end of the duct. If it is less than the speed of sound a further reduction in velocity takes place with an increase in pressure to match the decrease in kinetic energy. If the gas speed is sonic at the throat and there is a pressure drop available through the divergent part of the duct an increase in velocity takes place. The question must now arise why we do not always use a divergent duct if by this means an increase in velocity and in thrust can be obtained. The answer is, of course, that there are running conditions when the gas speed through the throat is less than sonic and when the divergent duct would actually reduce the velocity and the thrust. Furthermore if the duct diverges to such an extent that the outer diameter is larger than the engine casing, an increase in drag is introduced.

In Figs 47 and 48 it is possible to observe that the jet pipe converges to produce sonic velocity and the secondary nozzle formed by the petals in the open position (Plate 20) gives a divergent duct and supersonic velocity.

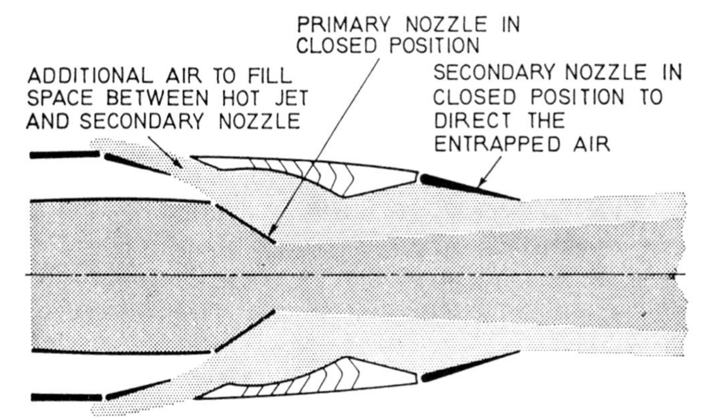

Fig. 47 Arrangement of primary and secondary nozzles for subsonic flight

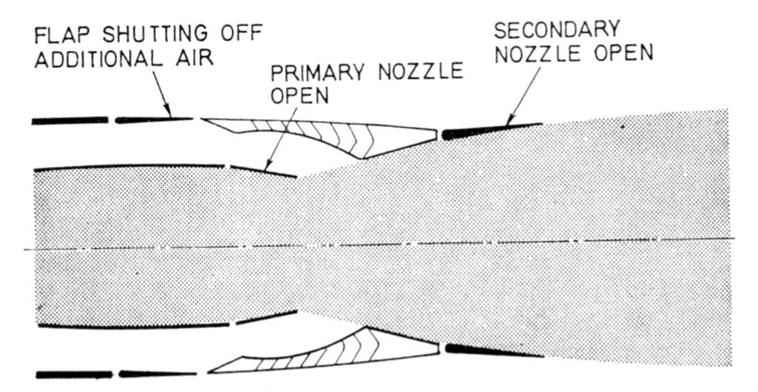

Fig. 48 Arrangement of primary and secondary nozzles for supersonic flight

80. Turboprops

When dealing with propulsion in Section 6 it was stated that the most economical way of obtaining thrust is by using the largest possible mass flow, with a low jet or slipstream velocity to avoid excessive kinetic energy losses. This particular aspect of economy is concerned only with the efficient use of the energy in the gas stream and not with the cost in terms of fuel burned to release the energy; propulsive efficiency here relates to jet velocity and aircraft velocity only, with no mention of fuel consumption. The formula linking them is a very simple one but no concern of ours provided the essential fact stated in the first sentence of this paragraph is understood.

Since the turbojet swallows the whole of the air used for propulsion and subjects it to the entire cycle, it is essential to keep the mass flow to the minimum to avoid excessive power absorption in the compressor. To compensate for a minimum mass flow the highest possible gas speeds must be used, and to get high propulsive efficiency with these high jet speeds the aircraft must be flown fast. If the jet velocity could be equal to that of the aircraft, but in the opposite direction, there would be no waste of kinetic energy and the propulsion efficiency would be 100 per cent. Unfortunately there is no thrust in this condition, so the case is of no practical value except as a pointer to the fact that the nearer jet velocity and aircraft velocity are to one another numerically (their directions are opposed) the better it is for propulsive efficiency.

Figure 1 shows that at low speeds the most efficient propulsion system is the propeller, which in the form of the propfan can offer high efficiency right up to jet speeds. Thus at the speeds of general aviation and most commuter transports it pays to accept the additional weight and complication of extra turbines and a reduction gear in order to drive a propeller. When used to drive a propeller the turbine has several advantages over the piston engine: higher powers are available for the same or even lower engine weight; there is always an element of jet thrust that becomes more efficient as the aircraft speed increases and compensates for the losses incurred by the propeller at higher speeds; the greater smoothness of the turbine compared with the piston engine provides more comfortable travel for the passengers; and the reduced vibration also leads to weight saving in the reduction gear, variable pitch mechanism, and in the blade, since these parts do not have to cope with the fatigue-promoting impulses of the piston engine. Moreover, today hardly any airports can supply fuel for large piston engines, because the gas turbine is so universal.

81. Turbofans

From the earliest days of jet propulsion it has been realized that the turbojet with its inherently high jet velocity must operate at a low value of propulsive efficiency except when conditions enable a high speed of flight to be used. The turboprop has already been mentioned as a means of using some of the energy in the hot gases to drive a propeller, so as to obtain the thrust with a large mass of air and a slipstream velocity very much less than the jet velocity of the turbojet.

Attaching a propeller to a turbine does not solve the problem of the serious losses incurred when any part of the propeller blade exceeds the speed of sound, and other means have to be considered of obtaining the desired combination of high mass flow and low velocity. A survey of the early Whittle patents shows that so much inventive genius was brought to bear on this subject that there is probably no propulsion system in existence that was not originally proposed in Whittle's name or that of his company, Power Jets Ltd.

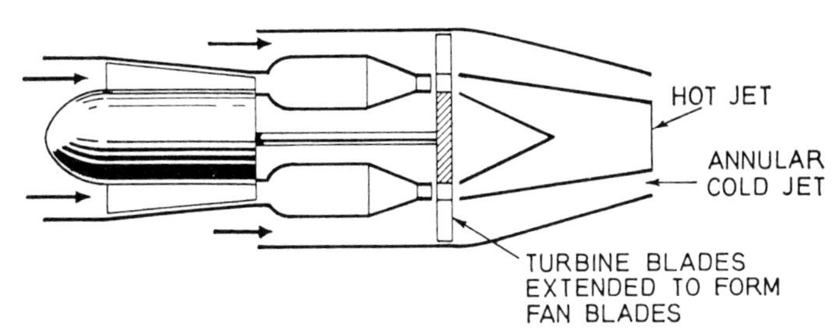

Fig. 49 Aft fan

The ducted fan was one such proposal, with various ways of driving the fan. In the method shown in Fig. 49 the turbine blades of an

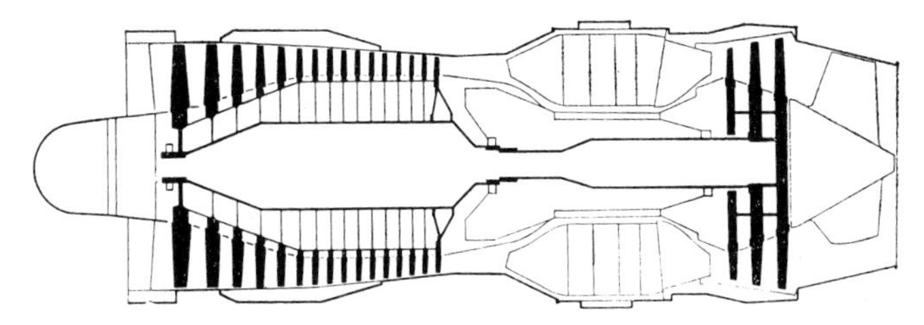

Fig. 50 Section through a Rolls-Royce Avon

Shows a straightforward turbojet in which the sixteen-stage axial compressor is driven by a three-stage turbine

otherwise orthodox jet engine are extended beyond the casing to act as short propeller blades operating inside a duct. Here the blades work in more favourable conditions than those of a normal propeller because ram increases the temperature and the speed of sound to a point not likely to be reached by the relatively small diameter multi-bladed fan. Little was done in this country to exploit this idea except for several prototype units built by Metropolitan-Vickers consisting of a fan driven by a separate turbine and designed for bolting to the jet pipe of the Metrovick F3. The Americans put two types of aft fan into service, one of about 4,000 lb thrust and the other of 16,000 lb, but no such engines have been designed for many years (if we exclude propfans).

Today virtually all turbofans have the fan on the front. This means it has to be driven by the low-pressure turbine via a long shaft passing down the centre of the engine. A few engines, including the ALF502 which powers the BAe 146, have a small high-speed turbine which drives the relatively large fan via a reduction gear (Plate 22). Obviously a front fan not only acts as a multi-blade propeller in accelerating air to the rear to form a propulsive jet but it also supercharges the power-producing core, or gas-generator, and thus by increasing the overall engine pressure ratio gives enhanced efficiency.

A key parameter in the design of a turbofan is BPR (bypass ratio), which is the ratio of mass flow (in unit weight per unit time, such as pounds per second) of the cold air bypassed around the core to the mass flow passing through the core. Some of the earliest turbofans had BPR of from 0.3 to 1.0. In Britain they were sometimes called bypass turbojets, and such a low BPR did little to reduce either fuel consumption or noise (Fig. 51). These engines were basically two-

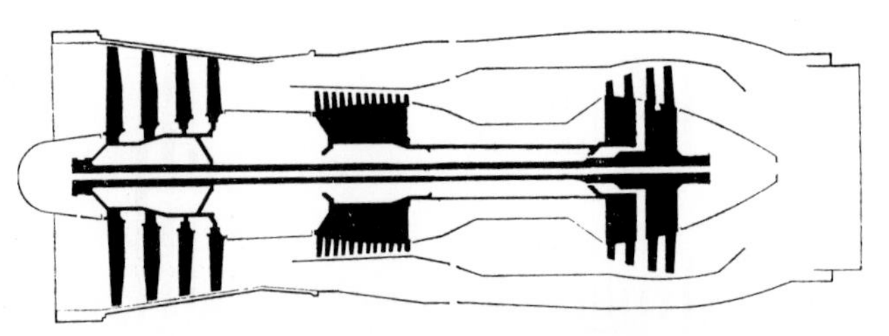

Fig. 51 Section through a Rolls-Royce Spey

Designed in 1959–60, this early turbofan was really a turbojet with an enlarged LP (low-pressure) compressor. About half its air was bypassed around the engine, the rest going through the HP compressor, combustion chamber and turbines. At the back there was no attempt to mix the two flows, as there would be today.

spool turbojets in which the LP compressor was slightly larger than necessary, so that the excess air could be bypassed. Today's turbofans are a different species. By adopting bold BPRs from 3 to 9 both fuel economy and noise have been dramatically improved. One of the latest engines (Figs 52 and 53) typifies the way these engines are dominated by the single-stage fan which, with its surrounding case, is far bigger than the slim core which drives it. As in most modern engines the five-stage LP turbine drives not only the fan but also three or four stages (four in the version shown) of LP booster com-

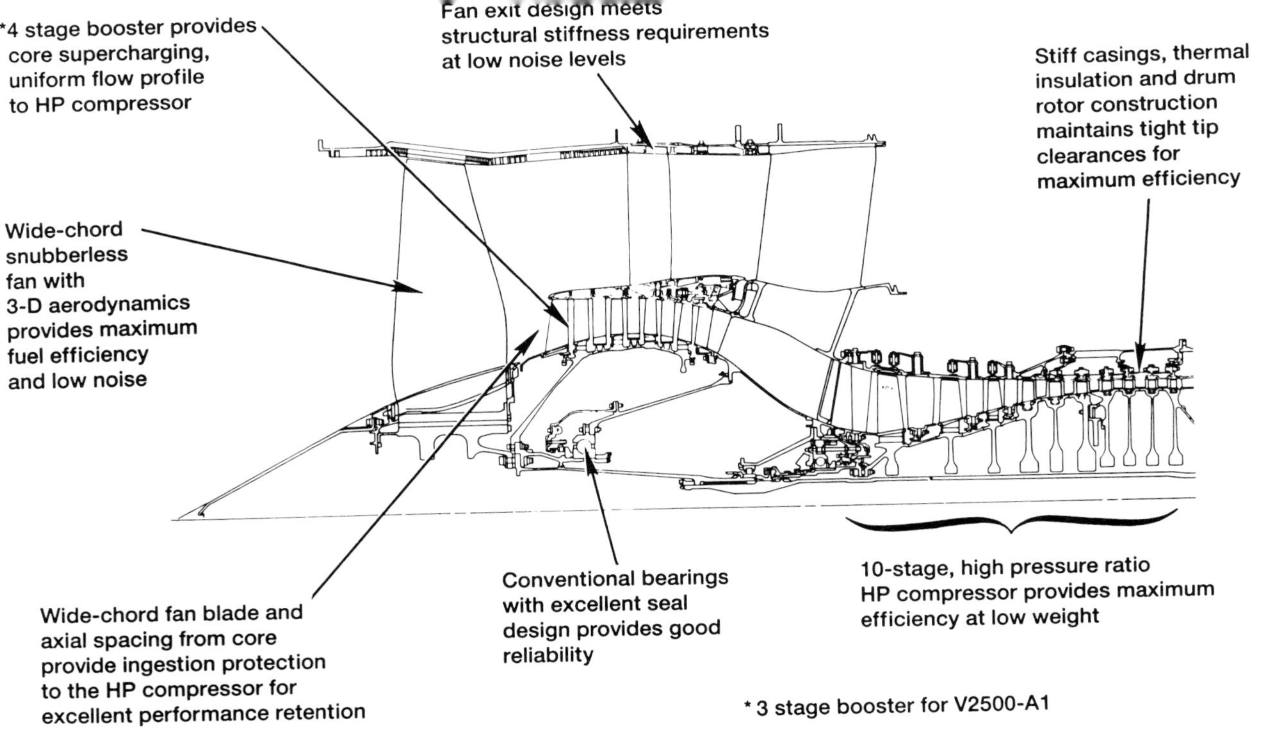

Fig. 52 A modern fan and compressor

This cross-section shows the fan and compressor section of the International Aero Engines V2500-A5, rated at 30,000 lb thrust. The wide fan blades are hollow, and need no part-span snubbers. The four-stage LP booster rotates with the fan. The HP inlet vanes and first three stators are variable. Overall pressure ratio is 32.5.

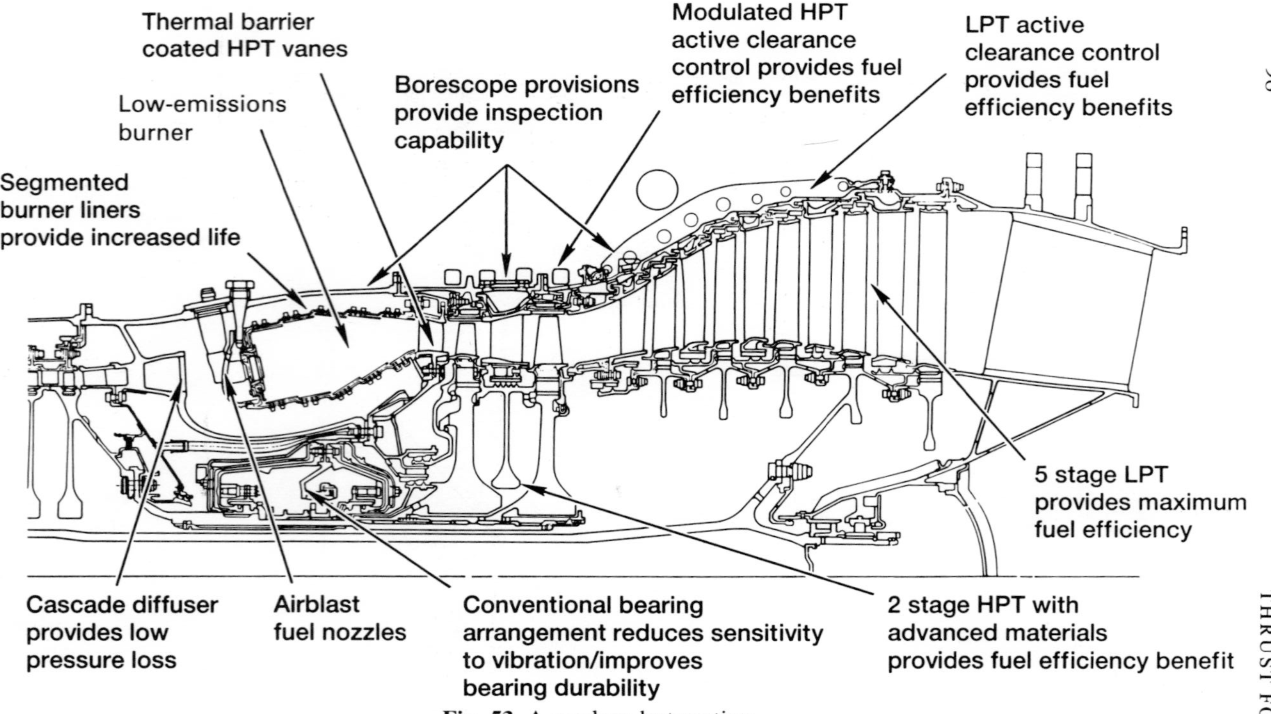

Fig. 53 A modern hot section

Drawn to a slightly larger scale than the front end (to which it connects) this drawing shows the V2500's combustion chamber and turbines. Borescopes are slim optical periscopes with which engine interiors may be examined without dismantling. HPT and LPT are the high-pressure and low-pressure turbines. Active clearance control is a method by which high-pressure air is blown all over the casing so that the gap around the tips of the moving blades is kept at a few thousandths of an inch, to minimise escape of gas.

pressor blades to increase overall pressure ratio, in this case to 32.5. In all such engines virtually all thrust comes from the fan; the core is merely there to drive it.

In the earliest HBPR (high BPR) engines, such as those produced to power the first generation of wide-body airliners, the fan had 45 to 50 blades of solid titanium, fitted with projections – called snubbers, clappers or part-span shrouds – to keep them properly spaced. Gradually designers learned how to make more efficient fans, with a smaller number of much larger blades, made of advanced composites or hollow titanium, and without any need for part-span shrouds, which caused drag and turbulence. Rolls-Royce pioneered this work, and also the development of full-length bypass ducts. Early fans rotated inside short ducts, blasting their huge supersonic airflow past the cowling over the core engine. The latest engines have full-length fan ducts (Plate 25), and at the back a mixer is fitted to cause rapid merging of the fan air with the hot jet from the core. This has a significant effect on fuel economy, and usually also reduces noise.

Modern HBPR engines are now being built to give thrusts up to 100,000 lb, a level considered fantastic even 20 years ago and quite unattainable by practical turbojets. Today turbojets are produced chiefly for simple expendable applications such as missiles, reconnaissance drones and targets. In the original edition of this book this section included a fairly extensive analysis of the pros and cons of turbojets and turbofans, but this is no longer relevant. The comparison began by assuming that both engines had the same mass flow, with LP compressors of the same size. Clearly with a BPR of 5 or more this cannot be done. If the turbojet were to have an LP compressor the same size as the turbofan's fan the resulting engine would be gigantic. Suffice to say, in general all modern jet aircraft use turbofans.

It is quite important to realize that the turbofan principle, however it is applied, does not add any energy to the air, it simply transfers some of the energy from the hot gases to the cold jet. This transfer of energy is only worth doing if the losses incurred in extracting the energy from the hot gas by means of a turbine are not so great that the gain in propulsive efficiency is largely offset.

In some by-pass systems there are two distinct jet streams, a high-speed hot jet and, surrounding it, a cold jet of lower velocity. A small gain in efficiency can be obtained by mixing the hot and cold jets before they leave the engine provided the action of mixing can be done without serious loss.

Because of the reduction in jet velocity turbofans are quieter than turbojets, a consideration of great importance when large multi-engined aircraft have to operate in the vicinity of towns. For engines of equal thrust the difference in noise level at the airport may be as great as 100 to 1. The values for perceived decibels laid down in current and future noise legislation are probably the most important single parameters affecting the design of every new civil engine. Prior to 1970 noise was almost taken for granted, and it became a serious menace. Gradually noisy airliners became not merely unacceptable but illegal. New aircraft have to comply with extremely stringent rules which get tougher all the time. Older aircraft are progressively having to be fitted with hushkits – which are expensive, heavy and reduce propulsive efficiency – or be re-engined, or simply be junked. By the early 1990s over 5,500 jetliners, whose airframes were nowhere near their fatigue limit, were facing withdrawal through inability to meet noise rules.

82. Thrust Reversal

It may seem out of place to include thrust reversal in the sections concerned with improving the performance, until it is realized that the ability to stop when required to do so may be every bit as important as the power to impart motion; only if the aircraft can be brought safely to rest can advantage be taken of the high performance available. Thrust reversal is obtained by swinging ducts into the jet stream and deflecting the efflux forwards to apply a considerable retarding force to the aircraft without causing wear and tear on tyres and brakes.

Two types of reverser are in common use. With turbojets and low-BPR turbofans they are installed on the jetpipe, the door (or clamshell) type swinging round to deflect the jet downstream of the nozzle. In the case of high-BPR engines, as used on modern airliners, the reverser deflects the fan air only, the residual thrust from the core being unimportant. How the two types work is shown in Fig. 54. The blocker door is simple. Four or more petal-type doors around the cowling simultaneously shut off the original duct and deflect the air diagonally forwards. In the cascade reverser the whole aft section of cowl translates (slides bodily) to the rear. This pulls down a ring of flaps which block off the fan duct, forcing the air to escape through a ring of curved cascade vanes which deflect it forwards.

83. Intakes

The simplest idea of an intake is a hole through which air is fed directly or through a duct to the engine, and for certain applications

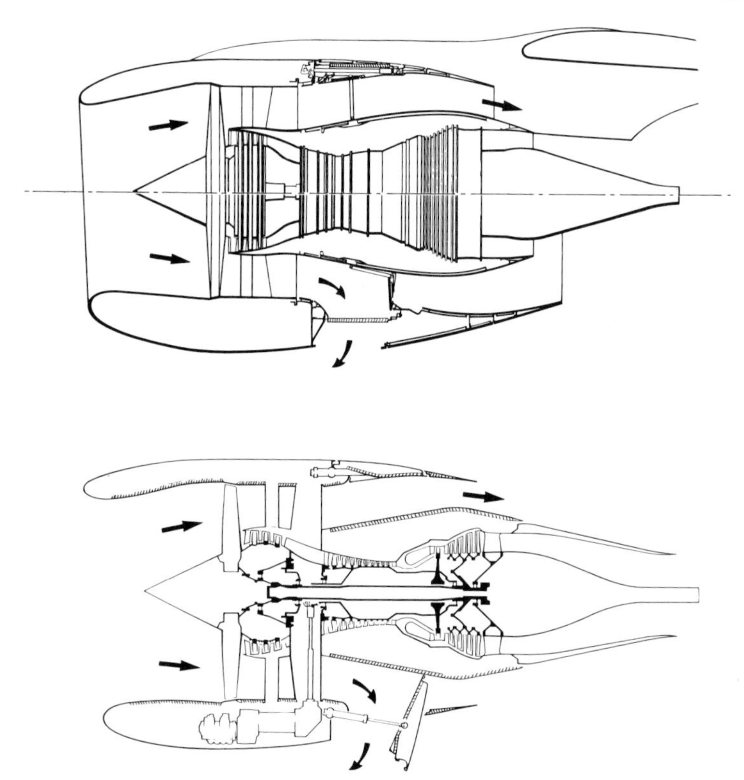

Fig. 54 Two basic forms of reverser for large fan engines are the cascade type (top) and door type (immediately above). Operation is explained in the text.

(By courtesy of Hispano-Suiza)

this is all that is required. However, no matter how simple the intake may be it is essential that it should handle the air without disturbing the flow and setting up eddies; the efficiency of turbo compressors suffers considerably if the air supplied is turbulent or hot. Intakes such as those used in podded installations or those placed in the nose of the aircraft disturb the airflow least of all, whereas the intakes used to supply buried engines are most likely to cause trouble as the air moves along in contact with the fuselage on its way to the intake. Careful detail design can keep the losses within bounds and the advantages of buried engines in certain aircraft types justifies the trouble that has to be taken to improve the flow conditions.

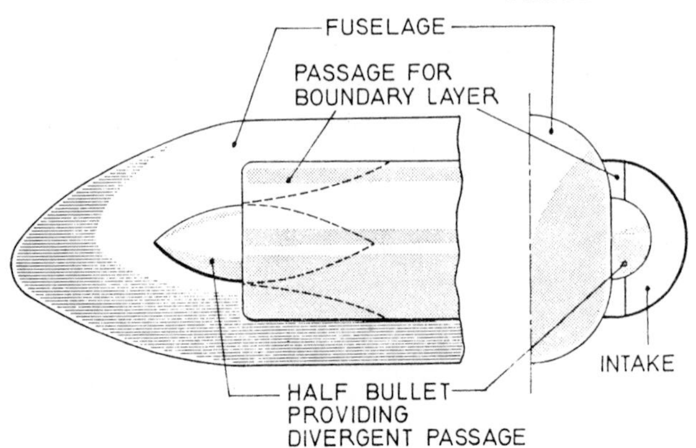

Fig. 55 One of a pair of fuselage mounted intakes with centre body and boundary layer passages

Figure 55 shows one of a pair of intakes mounted on the side of a fuselage; the intake actually stands slightly clear of the fuselage so that the turbulent boundary layer is allowed to pass between the intake and the fuselage and does not enter the intake where it would reduce compressor efficiency. The left diagram (which of course is purely schematic) shows the inlet from the side; the right diagram is a head-on view.

Aircraft speed has a very important effect on the shape and size of the intake and this effect may best be understood by following what happens inside and outside the intake as aircraft speed is increased. The compressor which is swallowing or trying to swallow the air which enters the intake is designed for a certain speed of the air at the moment it meets the first row of blades; excess speed at this point could, in conjunction with the speed of rotation, result in sonic speeds and their related losses. This condition can be regarded as placing a limit to the amount of air that enters the engine.

For the sake of simplicity let us assume that the compressor is designed to accept air which is travelling at about half the speed of sound as it approaches the compressor – a fairly normal value. When the engine is being run up on the ground the compressor has to do all the work of moving the air, which is almost bound to be travelling at something less than the maximum with which the compressor can cope. As the forward speed increases, breathing becomes easier for the compressor until the aircraft is flying at half the speed of sound, when the compressor is getting just the right amount of air at the right speed. Further increases in aircraft speed result in the air approaching the compressor at a higher speed than it is designed to accept. The speed must be reduced, and this opens up the prospect of recovering some of the kinetic energy possessed by the air. It has already been explained in Section 40 that this can be done by increasing the cross-section of the duct, so that the speed of the air is reduced and the pressure increased as the air passes from the mouth of the intake to the face of the first row of blades. Provided this recovery of energy is done smoothly it is a good thing; the force required to reduce the airspeed has to be applied anyway and it makes sense to use the work done in overcoming this force to do some of the work of compression. Remember, however, that turbulent flow must be avoided if at all possible otherwise the effort is simply wasted in producing eddies.

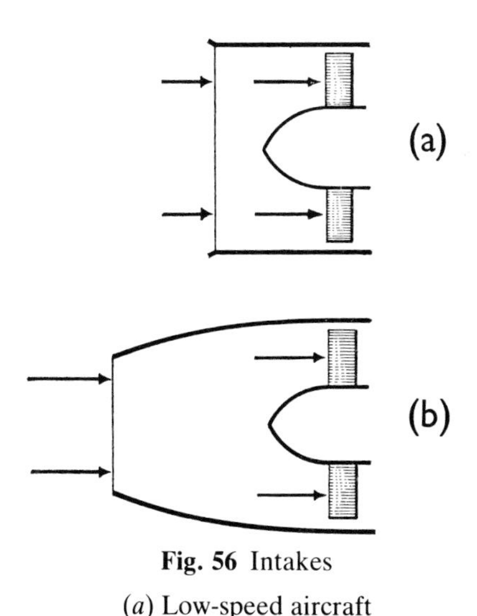

Fig. 56 Intakes

(*a*) Low-speed aircraft

Speed at intake less than maximum allowable at compressor

(*b*) High-speed aircraft

Airspeed reduced by diffusion to maximum allowable at compressor

Figure 56 shows a compressor with alternative intakes for low speed and for high speed; as the high-speed intake has a smaller mouth than the low-speed intake it is not ideal when used at speeds below those for which it was designed. In other words, some sort of variable intake is indicated, but unless speeds are going to be very high the weight and complication may not be justified. This brings up the very important point of just what does happen when speeds become very high.

So far, in tracing what happens in the intake it has been assumed that it is possible for the air to have its speed relative to the engine reduced to a value which will be acceptable at the compressor intake. What does 'relative to the engine' really mean? The air is at rest when it enters the intake, it is the intake that is moving. If the airspeed relative to the engine is reduced it means that the air is being hustled along in the direction in which the aircraft is moving. If the aircraft speed becomes high enough a point is reached when the air finds itself pushed right up to the speed of sound. When this happens shock waves are formed with a sudden rise of pressure in the zone immediately behind the waves. A lot of force is needed to give this compression and power is absorbed in doing it, but provided this compressed air is fed to the engine it contributes considerably to the total pressure rise before combustion takes place. As the speed of the aircraft gets higher the shock-wave system moves forward until eventually it is completely outside the intake. When this happens the exterior of the intake is exposed to the high pressure behind the wave and this pressure imposes a heavy drag on the cowling. When an intake with a centre body is used the position of the wave may be changed by adjusting the centre body. Alternatively spill doors may be opened between the mouth of the intake and the face of the compressor to allow air in excess of engine requirements to escape without having its velocity changed or having imposed drag on the nacelle. Sometimes the same door can be used as an inlet and an exit.

The Concorde intakes (Figs. 57 and 58) provide a good illustration of how complicated an intake may have to be to take full advantage of the energy recovery that is possible. At the speed of sound half the pressure rise may be due to ram and half to compression in the engine. At twice the speed of sound pressure ratios in the vicinity of 30 to 1 are possible and at three times the speed of sound this may rise to 50 to 1. As aircraft speeds increase the compression provided by the engine becomes relatively small and there is no need for complicated anti-surge devices such as variable incidence guide vanes and blow-off valves; the modest pressure rise over each of the compressor rotors is such that control of fuel flow alone provides sufficient safeguard against surge.

Note that in Fig. 57 the intake ramp which forms the upper wall of the duct is raised to give the maximum throat area and the auxiliary door is opened to face forwards and scoop in extra air to compensate for the absence of ram at low speeds and for intake dimensions suited to higher speeds. At supersonic speeds the ramp is lowered to give a

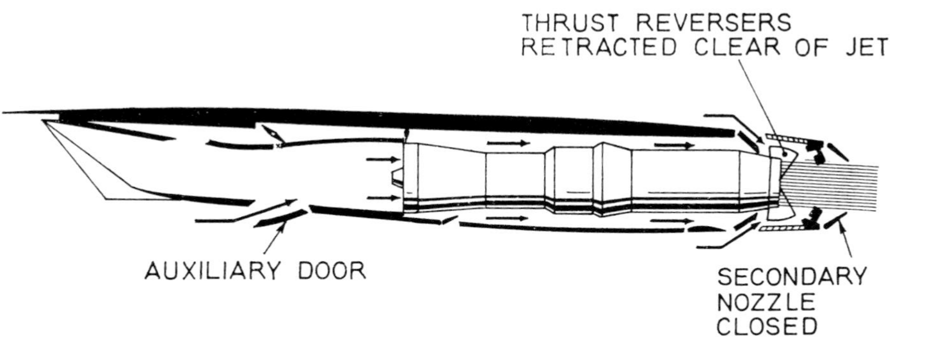

Fig. 57 At take-off and during flight at subsonic speeds an auxiliary door on the underside of the intake admits additional air. The tail pipe is adjusted to give the minimum opening to match the expansion ratio of about 3 to 1 which is available at these speeds

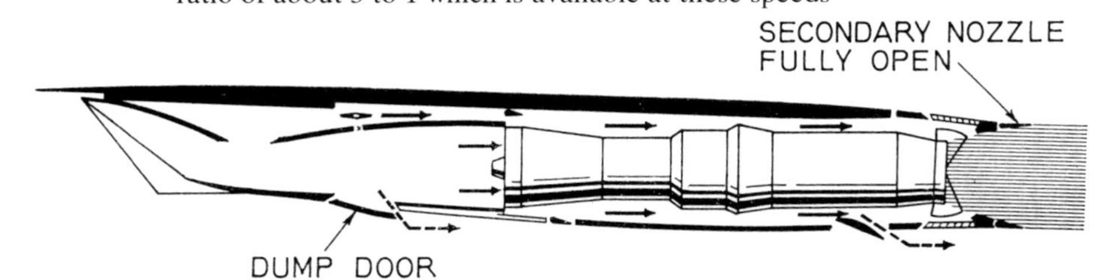

Fig. 58 At supersonic speeds a dump door in the intake is slightly open to get rid of air which is in excess of the engine's swallowing capacity. The jet pipe outlet is fully open to give the divergent orifice required with an expansion ratio of about 16 to 1 at $2\frac{1}{2}$ times the speed of sound

(Figs. 57 and 58 by courtesy of Rolls-Royce Ltd.)

very much smaller throat size so that there is diffusion of the air that has already been compressed at the shock wave.

84. Water/Methanol Injection

All engines are designed to give maximum power under certain stipulated conditions of atmospheric pressure and temperature and these are not always available when most wanted at takeoff. High temperatures on tropical airfields, low pressures on mountain airstrips, or a combination of both, may seriously reduce the power available and make it necessary to use some form of boosting. Injection of a mixture of water and methanol provides boost in interesting ways. Evaporation of the liquids cools the air throughout the compressor and at the entry to the combustion chambers; this restores the conditions on which the design was based and enables the full quota of fuel to be burned. Lowering the temperature at the compressor inlet improves the compressor efficiency, which means that less energy is absorbed by the compressor and more is available to give useful thrust. W/m injection is still used in a small number of aircraft powered by such engines as the J57 turbojet, Spey turbofan and Dart turboprop.

85. Engine Cooling

Much has been said in previous sections about the need to conserve the heat released by burning fuel and to convert as much as possible into useful work. Gas turbines normally require no external cooling system, but in the piston engine the cooling system carries away about as much heat as goes to do useful work. Pistons, cylinder heads, barrels and valves which are in contact with the burning mixture all get heat transferred to them, some of which must be taken away to prevent overheating and damage to the metals of which they are made. Before the metallurgists had developed suitable materials it was not unknown for piston crowns to collapse and for exhaust valves to lose their heads because of weakening by exposure to excessive temperatures. To this day exhaust valves still cause some concern and they are usually the first parts to show distress in an overworked engine.

Every designer of a piston engine for aircraft is faced with the choice of cooling his engine by air or by liquid. Air cooling has much to commend it. The objectives are to minimize the distance the heat has to travel from the white-hot gas in the cylinder and around the exhaust valve, and to maximize the area of the cooling fins around these hot regions. Even in the tropics the difference in temperature between the cylinder fins and the air will be well over 200°C, so air cooling seems the most efficient answer quite apart from the fact that it eliminates the need for a liquid cooling system.

Liquid cooling systems often use plain water, but usually are filled with water plus an additive such as ethylene glycol; a common mix is 40 per cent water and 60 per cent glycol, which can operate at 121°C. Liquid cooling obviously adds a closed circuit of piping, a pump and a radiator. Why, then, is it making such a powerful comeback in aviation? Among its advantages are higher efficiency and lower fuel consumption, better performance at altitude, less noise, less mechanical wear, reduced installed drag, longer life and longer TBO (time between overhauls). It is significant that the Continental engine on which Voyager relied on its unique non-stop flight around the world in December 1986 was a liquid-cooled type. Moreover, aircraft in which air-cooled engines have been replaced by liquid-cooled installations have invariably demonstrated not only quieter and smoother operation but also significantly enhanced flight performance.

Of course, a great deal depends on the application. Microlights and other ultralight machines, such as sport autogyros, invariably have an air-cooled engine installed in the simplest manner with no cowling or even baffles to direct air around the cylinder heads. Most light aircraft have horizontally opposed air-cooled engines with simple ram air inlets at the front of the cowling admitting to the space above the engine. Baffles then force the air to flow downwards around the cylinders, the heated air then escaping from a small gap between the bottom part of the cowling and the fuselage or nacelle downstream. Liquid-cooled engines are completely enclosed in a tight cowling which is perforated by various small low-drag ram inlets for the engine's own air for combustion and for the oil cooler (Plate 6). The main radiator may also be in a duct in the cowling (usually under the engine), but for minimum drag it may be elsewhere. In the small Super 2 aircraft it is recessed under the rear fuselage, while in the extremely fast RAM/Cessna 414AW (Plate 5) the two engines are cooled by radiators mounted horizontally in the flat tails of the nacelles.

The moving parts, particularly the pistons and exhaust valves, are the most difficult to cool; some of the heat from the piston crown is removed by oil splashed on the underside, and the remainder must be conducted to the piston rings and to the skirt for ultimate transfer to the cylinder through an oil film (or two films in the case of the sleeve valve engine). Since the oil plays a very important part in cooling the crankshaft bearings as well as the piston crowns it must have the heat removed from it in suitable radiators or by the provision of adequate sump surfaces.

During the years when exhaust valves were troublesome and unreliable complete fractures sometimes occurred, but much more often the faces split or pitted so seriously that the gas-tight seals were no longer effective. The exhaust valves have an unenviable existence as about one-quarter of the running time is spent with the heat of combustion on them and another quarter in the hot stream of exhaust gases. During the remainder of the running time conditions are less severe, and some of the surplus heat is off-loaded to the valve seat or possibly along the stem to the valve guide and so to the cylinder head and to the cooling system. Indifferent contact between stem and guide resulting from excessive clearance caused by wear can limit the heat removed in this way.

An effective but slightly costly solution to the valve cooling problem came to the fore with the successful development of the sodium-cooled valves already mentioned in Section 25. These valves are hollow and the cavity contains sodium which is molten at engine working temperatures. As the valves bob up and down the sodium splashes between the hot heads and the cooler stems, transferring heat at a greater rate than would be the case with solid stems. Sodium is a better conductor of heat than the steel it replaces and the violent agitation assists in the removal of heat from the valve head. Provided the clearance between the valve stem and the guide is not excessive sodium-cooled valves have a long life.

The sparking plugs also come in for a trying time, which is not made any easier by the conflicting requirements of different running conditions. If the electrodes are made massive to withstand the erosion caused by the sparking, they may be insufficiently hot when the engine is idling to burn off any oil deposited on the electrodes. Electrodes which are small so as to heat up quickly may become so hot when powers are high that they pre-ignite the charge before the spark takes place. The insulation must also be able to withstand wide temperature changes without mechanical or electrical breakdown. The development of suitable materials for electrodes and insulators has resulted in sparking plugs which are very reliable if serviced properly. As the heat has to be taken from the plug by conduction through the bosses in the cylinder head these bosses should be well cooled.

Attention has been focused on the pistons and exhaust valves because if proper provision is made for their cooling the other parts of the engine set no real problems. An adequate flow of coolant in the vicinity of the hot spots invariably results in satisfactory cooling everywhere else; in fact the greatest risk may be that some of the parts are overcooled. This has happened on some air-cooled engines in which cylinder finning was designed for appearance and not for the job it had to do, with the result that over-finning of the lower end of the cylinder barrel gave unequal cooling and produced distortion.

Early air-cooled engines were crudely installed with the cylinders merely projecting into the slipstream, and this is still common in slow aircraft, as noted earlier. In 1928 an Englishman, H. C. H. Townend, showed that radial engines could be cooled better and with lower drag by fitting a simple ring round them, the ring having a curved profile like a wing to give lift in a forwards direction (Fig. 59b). By the early 1930s this ring had been developed into long-chord cowlings which completely enclosed the engine, the airflow escaping via a controllable ring of gills or shutters at the junction with the fuselage or nacelle at the rear. Designers also found that cooling could be enhanced and drag further reduced by using the exhaust pipe(s) to blow through the cooling-air exit to draw through additional cooling airflow.

Gas turbines have no separate cooling systems and rely on using some of the vast excess of air that is passing through the engine to remove unwanted heat. The way in which some of this air is used to protect the flame tubes has already been mentioned; air is also blown over the turbine discs and in some cases through the blades so that these may operate at a temperature below that of the hot gases. All the heat that is picked up by the cooling air may earn its keep again as it mixes with the gases in the jet pipe before expanding to atmospheric pressure.

86. Controls

The control of large aircraft engines is of necessity a complex business, particularly when there are several of them and their performances have to be synchronized. Because of the need to make every pound of metal justify its existence aircraft engines must work very close to their limits, and safeguards must be provided to make sure that dangerous conditions of pressure, temperature or speed do not arise. The great complexity of modern engines and the intricate nature of the controls required justifies a high degree of automatic action. The ideal to be aimed at is to have a single lever controlling the whole range of output from idle to full power, and to entrust detail manipulations to fully automatic devices.

Control of power in the piston engine is effected by the throttle valve which, for any engine speed, can restrict the airflow to give less

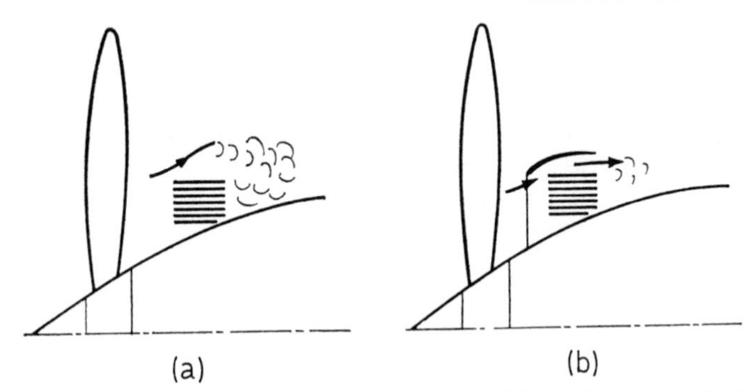

Fig. 59 (*a*) Turbulent airflow behind cylinder (*b*) Airflow controlled by cowling to reduce turbulence and drag

power than the maximum of which the engine is capable at that speed. The throttle is not in itself a speed control – indeed full throttle can be used over a wide range of speed dictated by the work the engine has to do. In aircraft applications speed is determined by the constant speed unit of the propeller control which, by altering the blade pitch, adjusts the load on the engine so that selected r.p.m. may be maintained.

Control of the turbine is effected by a manually operated valve in the fuel line between the pump and the burners. The basic setting of this valve is subject to modification by a variety of automatic devices to safeguard the engine. This direct control of the fuel flow differs fundamentally from the system used in piston engines, in which control is exercised over the amount of air consumed and the fuel flow adjusted to suit.

87. Supercharger Controls

Dealing first with the piston engine it does not appear necessary to go into any details about the function of the throttle valve, which simply lives up to its name and deprives the engine of air when restraint has to be placed on the power developed. However it may be as well to mention that it is the consumption of air in pounds per minute that is controlled and not the volume. At any given speed the volume of air consumed does not vary but the pressure in the induction manifold does; partial closure of the throttle reduces the pressure and the density of the air.

If a supercharger is designed to give sea-level pressure in the manifold when flying at considerable heights, it is capable of exerting dangerous pressures in the cylinders at much lower altitudes and must be controlled to prevent damage. Ideally the supercharger should be controlled by adjusting the speed relative to that of the crankshaft, and one of the attractions of the exhaust-driven turbo-supercharger is the ease with which this can be done by controlling the flow of exhaust gases to the turbine. When a mechanical drive is used some degree of speed control is obtained by the use of gears giving the choice of two, three or four different ratios. Because of the complications involved it is seldom possible to justify more than two ratios, which is not enough without the application of throttling. This in a way is a disappointing state of affairs, as under certain flying conditions the throttle has to be used deliberately to depress the pressure so that when the supercharger raises it again a safe value of pressure is not exceeded.

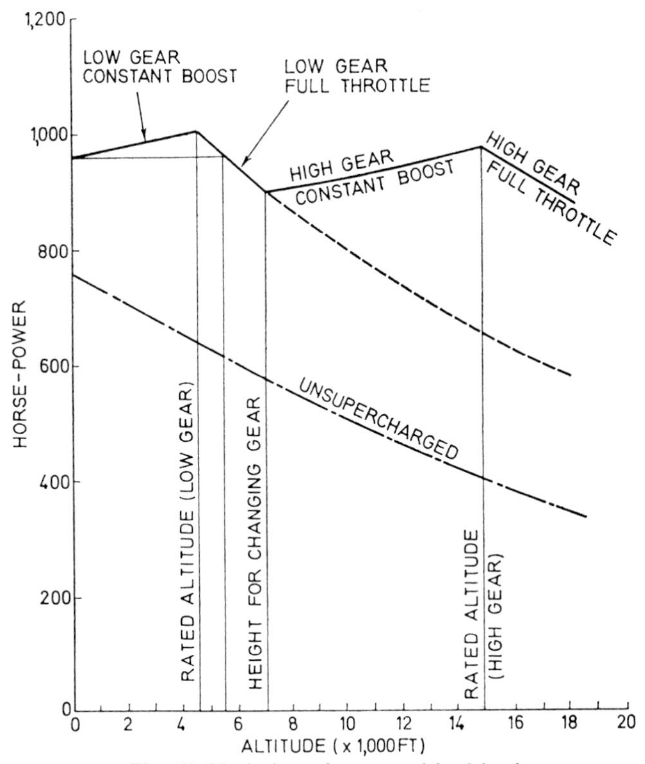

Fig. 60 Variation of power with altitude

Figure 60 shows some interesting facts about the performance of a particular engine at various heights and compares what the engine could do in the normally aspirated state with the performance when using a two-speed supercharger. Sections 35 and 36 gave details of the need for supercharging and how the centrifugal compressor is used to make good the decrease in atmospheric pressure as altitude increases. A study of Fig. 60 will bring out several points about supercharging not already mentioned.

When used at sea-level some restriction must be placed on the air consumption of the engine by partly closing the throttle, to avoid producing excessive pressures in the manifold. As the aircraft climbs the throttle is progressively opened to compensate for the decreasing density of the atmosphere and to maintain constant boost pressure in the inlet manifold. Constant boost pressure in the manifold results in a slight increase in power as the aircraft climbs because of reduced back pressure at the exhaust and reduced pressure in the crankcase. The reduced back pressure at the exhaust leads to improved scavenging and improved filling of the cylinder at the next induction stroke, whilst the reduced pressure in the crankcase renders the pressure in the cylinder more effective.

When the altitude is 4,500 feet in this particular case, the throttle is fully open; this altitude is known as the *rated altitude* or *full throttle height* above which it is impossible to maintain sea-level power unless the supercharger speed is increased by changing into a higher gear. However the change is delayed in this example beyond the altitude of 5,500 feet at which the power has dropped to what it was at sea-level. The actual change takes place at 7,000 feet and as soon as the supercharger is in high gear it is necessary to close the throttle slightly to avoid over-boosting. During the climb to 15,000 feet the throttle is progressively opened until at that height it is once more fully open; this is the rated altitude (high gear) for this particular supercharger. If the climb is continued above this height the power decreases until there is only just enough of it to maintain height but not enough to climb any further.

There may be a temptation to wonder why high gear is not used all the way up from sea-level, but the answer is that so much power is lost in the gearing and in forcing the air past the partly closed throttle that the use of an excessively high gear at low altitudes results in less power at the crankshaft. The change from low to high gear is usually made at the height at which the power available in high gear just overtakes the power in low gear.

To get the best performance from the engine and at the same time avoid dangerous pressures, requires a careful watch on the boost pressure gauge and continual adjustment of the throttle. When two or perhaps four engines are involved and performances have to be synchronized some form of automatic control is almost essential.

88. Automatic Boost Control

Figure 61 shows a very simple automatic boost control shorn of all trimmings and finer adjustments. In the configuration shown the engine is assumed to be idling, with the manifold pressure well below the rated value. Movement of the hand control lever towards the open position moves the throttle valve so that less restriction is placed on the ingoing air. Pressure in the manifold starts to rise and if the throttle is sufficiently far open the prescribed maximum pressure will be reached in a very short time. An aneroid attached to the control valve consists of a stack of thin metal capsules which contract under the influence of the increased pressure and raise the control valve, so that high-pressure oil is directed to the upper side of the servo piston and the lower side is vented to the oil return. Movement of this servo piston cranks the link between the hand lever and the throttle sufficiently to close the throttle enough to keep the manifold pressure at a safe value. If the aircraft climbs with the linkage cranked, the falling pressure allows the aneroid to expand and reverse the previous flow to the servo piston. The resulting movement of the servo piston straightens the link from the hand lever and opens the throttle far enough to restore the boost pressure. It should be understood that whenever the rated boost is obtained in the manifold the aneroid returns the control valve to the neutral position, thus isolating the servo piston from the oil supply lines.

Figures 62 and 63 show in diagrammatic form two more elaborate automatic boost controls for use in different engines. In the device shown in Fig. 62 a floating lever takes the place of the divided link of Fig. 61. The action may perhaps be most readily understood from a description of what happens as the hand control is moved from the idle to the full power condition when operating at sea-level. The movement of the hand lever is conveyed to the throttle through the two bell crank levers and the floating lever, which may tilt about any one of the three pivot points. The increase in manifold pressure which results from opening the throttle causes contraction of the aneroid and this in turn lifts the control valve so that oil passes to the upper surface of the servo piston. As the piston goes down the floating lever tilts and the motion reduces the throttle opening. This process goes on until the boost pressure reaches the rated value and the aneroid returns to the original length and cuts off further oil flow

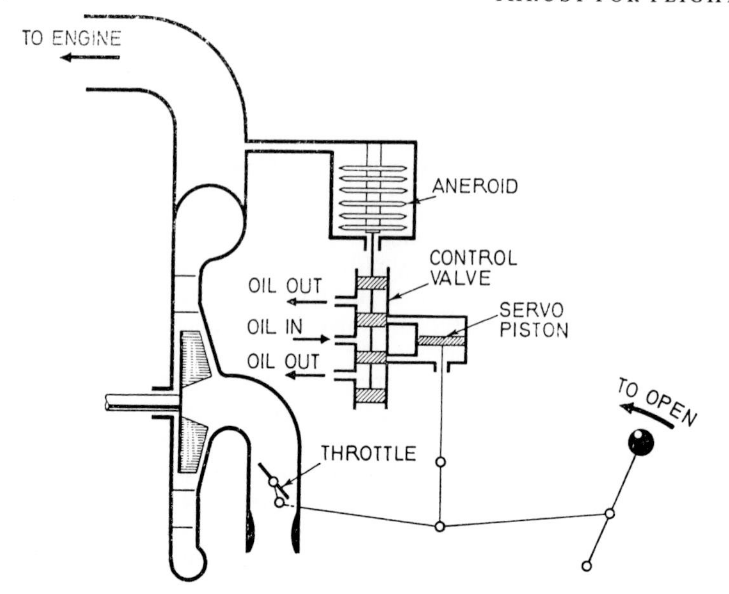

Fig. 61 Simple automatic boost control

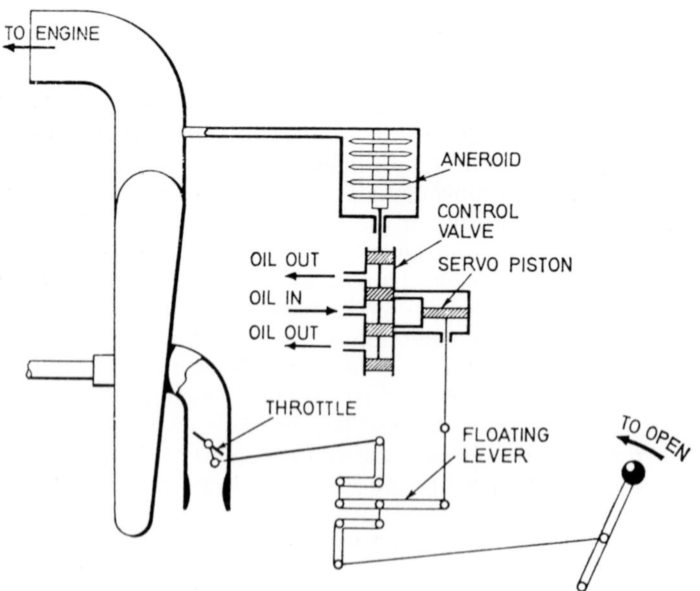

Fig. 62 Floating lever linkage in automatic boost control

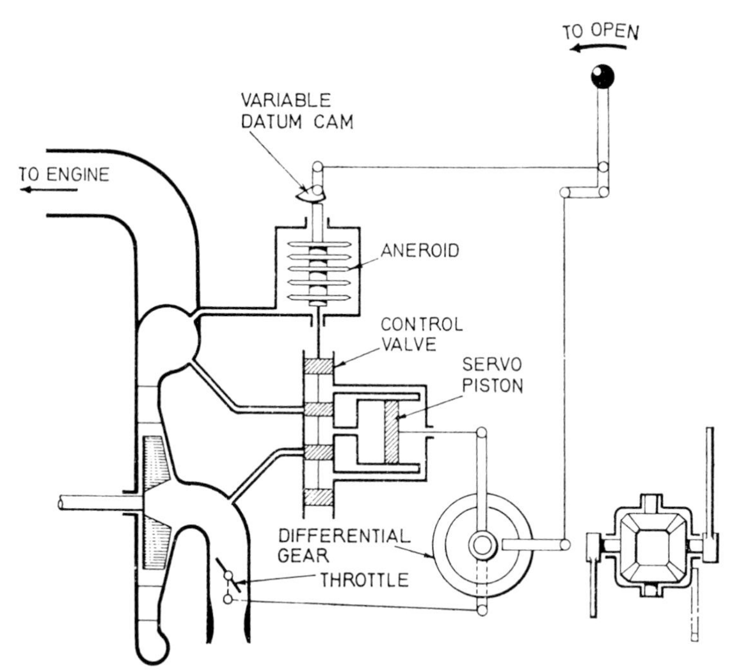

Fig. 63 Automatic boost control with differential linkage

to or from the servo piston. If the aircraft now climbs steadily, the expansion of the aneroid directs high-pressure oil to the underside of the piston, and the floating lever is tilted so that the bell crank lever and the throttle are moved towards the open position. As the climb continues this process goes on until the throttle is fully open at the rated altitude. The reverse sequence is followed on descent.

In the mechanism shown in Fig. 63 the place of the floating lever is taken by a differential gear. With the hand lever fixed in any position, rotation of the right-hand bevel by the lever linked to the servo piston results in rotation of the left-hand bevel and with it the lever connected to the throttle. The fact that levers rotate in opposite directions to one another is not important provided allowance has been made for this in the design. In this way the aneroid and piston have complete control of the throttle position up to the limit set by the hand lever.

To study another action of the differential gear, the connection to the servo should be regarded for the moment as a fixture. Movement of the hand lever forces the casing to turn on the fixed spindle and makes the planet bevels rotate on their own axes. This causes the bevel connected to the throttle to turn in the same direction as the casing (and incidentally at twice the speed). In this way the throttle is controlled by the hand lever and it is only when manifold pressure threatens to exceed the prescribed amount that the aneroid contracts enough to bring the servo piston into action to override the hand control if necessary.

This particular control system uses the boost pressure to operate the servo, whereas that illustrated in Fig. 62 uses high-pressure oil from the engine lubrication system. It is safe to assume that the two methods are equally effective; had it been otherwise only the better one would have survived.

Descriptions of boost controls would be incomplete without reference to the variable datum devices employed. In the simple automatic control shown in Fig. 61 full power is obtained at sea-level by a very small movement of the hand lever and the rest of the travel is just so much lost motion. Such an arrangement makes sensitive control very difficult at low altitudes and calls for modification of the device in the following way.

If, instead of fixing the top of the aneroid to the casing as in Fig. 61, this is anchored by a screw, it is possible to adjust the boost pressure at which the control valve and servo piston come into action. Pushing the top of the aneroid down makes it necessary to have a higher pressure in the manifold to bring the servo into action to prevent further opening of the throttle, and the reverse applies when the screw is turned back to allow the aneroid to come up. So that the datum selected may be related to the hand lever position a cam, or cams, are linked to the lever so that the aneroid is depressed as the lever is moved to open the throttle. In this way the control gives a high boost pressure for large throttle openings and vice versa.

A review of what has already been said about controls for the piston engine shows that speed is held to a selected value by means of the propeller constant-speed unit (Section 11), mixture strength is regulated to suit various altitudes by means of some form of aneroid operated control, and boost pressure is kept within the safe limits at sea-level and to a constant value as the aircraft climbs to its rated altitude.

In the realms of ignition the timing of the spark is seldom left to the pilot or the engineer. There may be a centrifugal advance mechanism, to make sure that at the very low speeds of starting the ignition is sufficiently retarded to avoid backfire and that it is advanced as speed increases to ensure complete combustion in the shorter time available. There may also be a link with the throttle, or a pressure operated device, to retard the ignition slightly at those throttle openings that give high cylinder pressures and tend to promote detonation.

The extent to which automatic devices are used in the piston engine to achieve single lever control over the whole range of operation sets a standard to be followed in the aircraft turbine.

89. Controls for the Aircraft Turbine

Reference has already been made in Section 86 to the fact that turbines are controlled by regulating the flow of fuel to the combustion chambers. In the simpler installations, control is exercised by the manipulation of a valve placed in the main fuel line between the pump and the combustion chambers, with various automatic devices to modify the flow so as to avoid critical conditions. When re-heat is used or when the aircraft has to fly at supersonic speeds it is necessary to provide controls for the intake (Section 83) and for the jet pipe orifice (Section 79). To live up to the ideal of a single control to cover the whole range from idle to full power some degree of complication is inevitable.

The purpose of some of the automatic controls which are superimposed on the manual setting is quite obvious, as in the case of those used for maximum speed and for jet pipe temperature, but the functions of some of the others may appear to overlap. This may well be so, because even for example the apparently simple matter of regulating the fuel flow by the manually operated valve is subject to many variations at different fuel pressures and orifice sizes. These control systems have grown up as a result of experience and careful analysis of running conditions.

90. Limiting the Speed

The means used for limiting the maximum speed may be a simple mechanical governor mounted on the pump spindle as shown in Fig. 40. When the limiting speed is reached the force set up by the rotating weights is sufficient to open one of the valves and reduce the pressure on the spring side of the servo piston, which allows the piston to move to the right and repositions the cam plate so as to deliver less fuel to the engine and thus prevent an unwanted increase in speed. In some engines the flyweights are replaced by what is in effect a small centrifugal pump which builds up sufficient pressure to initiate control changes at the required speed. Plate 42 gives an idea what a mechanical governor really looks like – the flyweights are just visible at the cut-away near to the driving end and the spring is obvious at the right.

91. Pressure Control

Control of fuel flow relative to engine speed alone is not sufficient, and it is necessary to make allowances for changes of pressure at the intake which may arise from changes of forward speed or of altitude. In Fig. 40 a simple aneroid capsule is contained in a chamber which is subject to the intake pressure, and the free end of the aneroid is in proximity to the stem of a valve in the servo piston pressure system. Low pressures allow the aneroid to expand and open the valve so as to relieve the pressure and reset the cam plate to give a reduced fuel flow to match the reduced air density. Actual pressure controls are necessarily more complicated than the one shown because both the aneroid movement and the force it can apply are in fact very small. Usually a system of levers, springs and diaphragms is needed to give the fine state of balance required to ensure that the small responses of the aneroid can initiate the necessary control changes. Figure 64

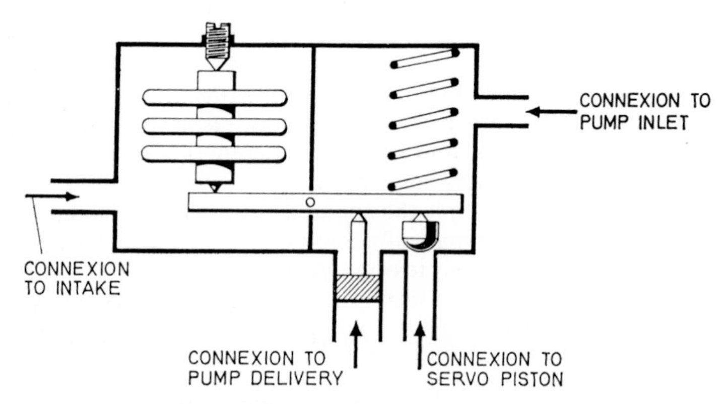

Fig. 64 Barometric pressure control

shows one of these controls in diagrammatic form, with the aneroid in the left-hand chamber where it is exposed to the same pressure as in the intake. The top end of the aneroid bears on an adjustable stop, and the bottom on a lever which is mounted in a flexible diaphragm serving the double purpose of providing a pivot and separating the two chambers of the control. The lever is kept in balance by the combined forces of the aneroid, a spring, and a push rod loaded by the pressure in the fuel pump delivery. A valve connected to the pressure system of the pump servo piston, as described in Section 66, is normally held on its seat by the combined effect of the various forces on the lever. The balance of forces may be upset by a drop in the intake pressure or an increase in the fuel line pressure and initiate a reduction in fuel flow to match the changed conditions, either of which could lead to overheating if no action were taken.

92. Anti-surge Devices

Traditional BPCs (barometric pressure controls) often used a simple screw stop above the aneroid, as in Fig. 64. Alternatively the lower end of the aneroid could be attached to a diaphragm. A comparison of two typical BPCs shows that the biggest difference between them is found at the lower end of the aneroid spindle. In the first there is a simple screw stop to limit the lever movement, but in the second the lower end of the aneroid is carried in a flexible diaphragm separating the aneroid chamber which is at atmospheric pressure, from the lower chamber which is at compressor delivery pressure. The lever in this case comes under the action of a number of forces; these are set up by the aneroid, the pressure difference between atmosphere and compressor delivery, fuel pressure in the burner line, and by the spring load. The valve in the servo system may be opened by excessive pressure in the fuel line, reduced compressor delivery pressure, or a combination of both; all are factors which could upset the desired proportions of fuel to air and lead to surging.

A further and fairly similar control responds to the pressure rise across the compressor, but with no element of fuel line pressure as in the two previous cases. This is a pressure ratio limiter which also acts in some respects as a speed control, because rising speed usually takes with it an increase in pressure ratio within the design range.

93. Temperature Control

The gas turbine is by its very nature a hot-running engine, with temperatures in the neighbourhood of 2,000°C in the centre of the combustion zone. Although suitable mixing with excess air reduces this temperature somewhat and the manner in which the air is introduced shields the metalwork from the worst of the blast, the gases are still very hot as they approach the turbine. For efficiency and power this is essential, provided there is an adequate pressure drop available to convert the heat to work at the turbine or to kinetic energy in the jet pipe. Whilst everything possible is done to cool the blades, the gas temperature must be kept as high as practicable within limits that ensure a reasonable life for the blades. Observation of the high temperatures of the gases at the turbine entry is not an easy matter, but it is fairly simple to measure the temperature in the jet pipe. As the latter temperature bears a calculable relationship to that at the turbine entry, for it is lower by an amount that depends on the energy extracted from the gas in doing work on the turbine, it is shown on the instrument panel and used to initiate control when a reduction in fuel flow is indicated to avoid destructive temperatures.

The simple jet pipe temperature control shown in Fig. 40 depends on the expansion of a rod which is exposed to hot gases to initiate reductions in fuel flow. One end of the rod is fixed and the other makes contact with a valve in the servo circuit so that when the temperature reaches a prescribed limit there is sufficient expansion to lift the valve and bring about the required modification in fuel flow. In some respects control of temperature in this way is a fuel/air ratio control as the temperature in the jet pipe depends on the proportions of fuel and air, but because of the time lag between the temperature rise and the operation of the control it does not act quickly enough to prevent surge.

94. Afterburner Control

An afterburner (Section 78) has to be lit up in a carefully controlled sequence. The control system used varies, but in one common arrangement when the power lever is rocked across and moved forward into afterburner the reheat fuel is first fed to a pilot burner downstream of the turbine. This provides a tongue of flame which can light up the main reheat rings as soon as fuel reaches these from the air-turbine pump via a spring-loaded valve which serves two functions. It ensures that the reheat fuel is at full pressure and flow from the very start, and it also holds back main afterburner operation until the variable nozzle has opened.

95. Electrical Fuel-Control Systems

In really large aircraft it is almost impossible to run mechanical controls from the pilot's cockpit to four or more engines which may either be buried in the wings or suspended in pods under the wings. In following the devious paths involved some lost motion would be inevitable, with stiffness or inadvertent operation brought about by flexing of the aircraft structure. Electrical devices offer a much more precise way of achieving remote control. Installation problems are only concerned with supporting the cables and routeing them clear of obstacles, flexing of the structure can be accommodated with no

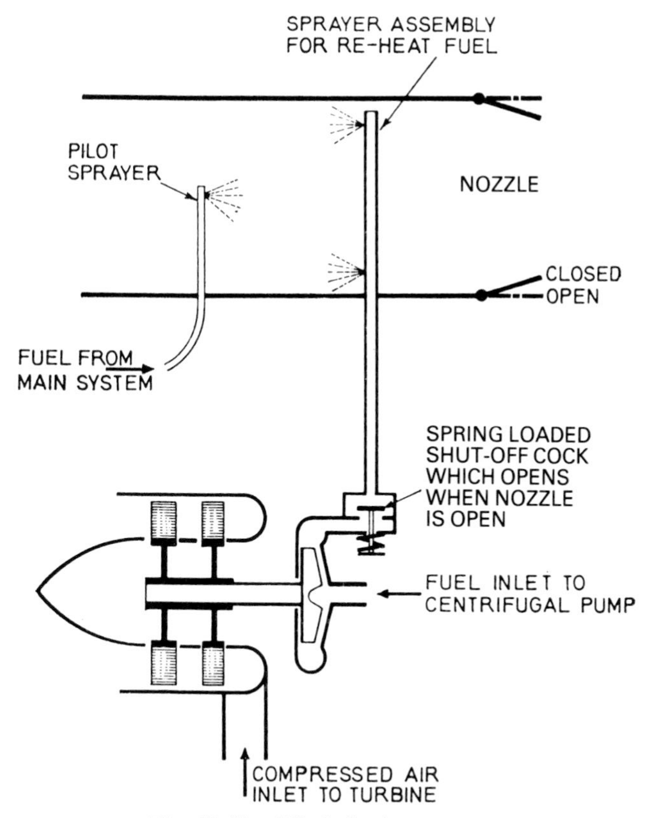

Fig. 65 Simplified afterburner system

adverse effects, and components may be located where conditions of temperature and vibration are less severe than on the engine. Some of the variables that have to be measured in the turbine are most conveniently done electrically, for example temperatures in the jet pipe can be measured by thermocouple and those in the intake by resistance thermometer. Assemblies depending on transistors offer considerable weight saving through miniaturization, and in some cases simple electrical circuits do the work of the mechanical assemblies they replace. A good example of this is the use of an electromagnetic core, shaped to span the teeth of a gear wheel and initiate signals which indicate the shaft speed without the introduction of any moving parts additional to those already in existence; the frequency of the current induced in the circuit is proportional to the speed of the gear and with suitable calibration can be used to indicate r.p.m.

Although the change from mechanical to electrical controls now seems an obvious one to make, it took a long time for engineers and operators, accustomed to mechanical systems which could be seen to work, to gain confidence in a collection of mysterious components which did the same complicated tasks without any obvious fuss. The mechanically minded maintenance man, used to detecting faults by visual inspection, was at first inclined to blame major assemblies when anything went wrong, even though such details as dirty or loose connections actually accounted for most of the faults that occurred. The electronics industry had also to struggle against an unfortunate reputation acquired under competitive pressure in the radio and television business. It took the success of the Britannia, with thousands and thousands of trouble-free flying hours, to establish all-electrical controls as an acceptable system.

96. Jet Pipe Temperature Control

Electrical controls made a modest start quite early in the jet age when thermocouples were used to determine jet pipe temperatures and to start off the control sequence needed to limit flow when temperatures became too high. A thermocouple consists of two materials which produce a small current when heated in contact with each other. The output from the thermocouple is amplified and used either to energize a solenoid-operated valve situated in the main fuel line between the manually controlled throttle valve and the burners or to give a temperature reading at the instrument panel.

An interesting point arises about temperature readings made in a moving gas stream because the thermometer or other measuring device will arrest the progress of some of the gas stream, converting kinetic energy to heat and recording a higher temperature than would have been the case if the relative velocity had been zero. It is seldom an easy matter to tell how much of the kinetic energy is accounted for in the final reading, and often it does not matter when the readings are comparative and our concern is with whether the temperatures are higher or lower than normal. When calculations are based on temperature it is necessary to recognize what the readings represent: *static temperatures* are those registered when there is no relative motion between gas and thermometer, and *total head temperatures* are those registered when the thermometer is held at rest in the moving stream and the gas is brought to rest at the thermometer bulb. The relationship between temperature and velocity is an important one with many applications in aircraft and engine calculations. It enables accurate estimates to be made of the temperature in the intake because of ram, or of the increase in velocity to be expected when a gas expands between known conditions of temperature and pressure before and after the expansion, to quote but two examples.

97. Complete Electrical Control

A book which adopts a non-mechanical approach to a technical subject is no place in which to enlarge on the internal workings of the many components that go to make up a modern control system; there are said to be several hundred electronic components in each of the Concorde engines and no doubt there are many miles of wire connecting them. Fortunately it is possible to understand the purpose of the components without having an electronic engineer's knowledge of how they do their work. When we look around it is surprising how many automatic devices we rely on in our homes and in our motorcars without a thought about their whereabouts let alone how they work. Thermostats look after the temperatures in refrigerators, clocks switch the central heating on and off as required, and the output of car generators is automatically adjusted to the electrical load and state of the battery. We obviously have faith in these devices except when our curiosity is aroused! From now on our concern will be with the contribution made by the components to a complete control system and not with what goes on inside the components.

Figure 66 is a block diagram representing a control system, with one basic circuit linking the pilot's control lever to the throttle valve and two subsidiary circuits with power to override the manual control should the shaft speed or the jet pipe temperature become excessive. The two Selsyns with their connecting circuit provide the link between the pilot's lever and another on the engine control unit. When the pilot's lever is moved out of a predetermined position relative to that on the control unit, a current flows in the connecting circuit in such a direction as to restore the original relative positions. No matter how quickly the pilot's lever is moved the rate at which the throttle can be opened is limited to a rate known to provide engine acceleration which is safe from surge. The detail work in some of these modifying circuits is rather ingenious and to the mechanically minded they may appear to be a bit uncanny in the way they assess values, compare them with other values, and decide from a number of signals which to ignore and which require action. Much of the decision making depends on comparing the strengths of two signals, one of which is reporting on the state of affairs at some point in the engine and the other from a standard source which may be a simple

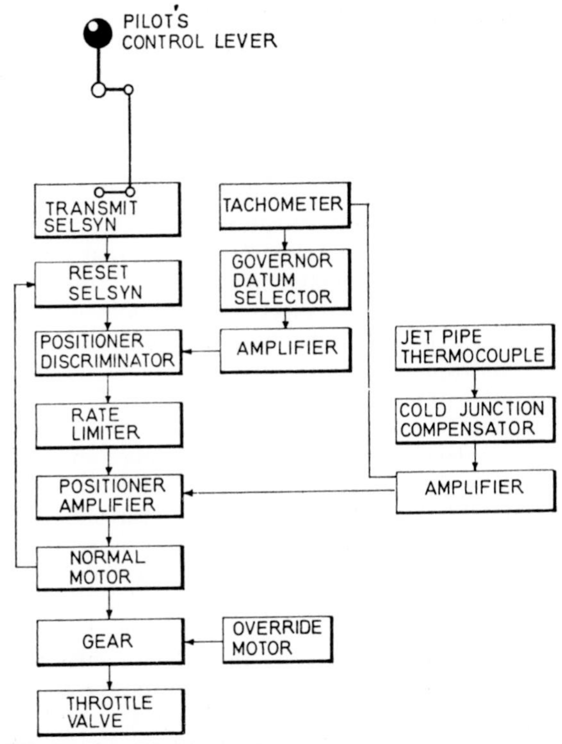

Fig. 66 Simplified block diagram of turboprop controls

cell or a thermocouple placed so as to give atmospheric temperature as a datum. It is also possible to compare the electrical signals from such widely different things as compressor speed and delivery temperature, so that if the temperature is higher than it should be at any given speed this can be treated as a warning of surge on the way. This situation could be met by reducing the rate at which the throttle is being opened, even to the point of stopping it altogether if the threat of surge has occurred during acceleration.

The control system represented in Fig. 66 is for a turboprop in which the propeller is driven by the low-pressure turbine and controlled to a constant speed as described in Sections 11 and 19. As the high-pressure turbine drives the compressor and also receives the first blast of hot gas straight from the combustion chambers, this assembly has to deal with the problems of maximum cycle temperature and of surge. Information on temperature and speed are supplied to the control system by this section of the engine.

The diagram shows that the throttle motor drive passes through a gearbox on its way to the throttle valve, and another drive comes into the gearbox from an override motor. This motor is supplied with current from a completely separate source and provides an emergency system which can be brought into use in the event of failure of the main system.

Plate 45 shows how the components of the electrical control are combined in several units. These units give no indication of the complicated circuits involved, which makes it easy to understand why they are so often described as black boxes.

98. Control System for a Two-Spool Turbojet with Re-heat

Today most engines have electronic control, but there are still many with traditional hydromechanical controls. A typical set of block diagrams for a turbojet with afterburner are shown in Figs. 67, 68 and 69. The first links the pilot's power lever to the throttle on the engine, the second connects the same lever to the afterburner and the third automatically controls the variable nozzle.

The first problem that crops up is why there should be two circuits coming out of the pilot's selector instead of one. The one marked 'position datum' is used to position the throttle during starting and the other sets the throttle according to the speed selected by the control lever once the engine is running. The box marked 'highest wins' indicates a device which determines the circuit to be chosen. It is probably easy enough to realize that during starting there can be little or no speed signal and therefore the signal from the position circuit will win; once the speed has built up the change-over takes place and control is based on the speed selected.

The basic circuit contains a rate limiter to prevent too rapid opening of the throttle. Three computers for acceleration, temperature and pressure can influence the signals which reach the throttle motor. The acceleration computer is supplied with information about temperature and pressure conditions in the intake and about the speed of the high-pressure compressor; if this information indicates that the engine is accelerating more rapidly than it should do a switch is opened to halt, but not reverse, the throttle motor.

The main function of the maximum temperature computer is obvious enough – to watch that the jet pipe temperature does not exceed a limit determined by experience – but there is also an important subsidiary function. This is to observe how rapidly the temperature rises, for in this way an early indication can be given that all is not well, possibly the first signs of surge beginning to show. Correc-

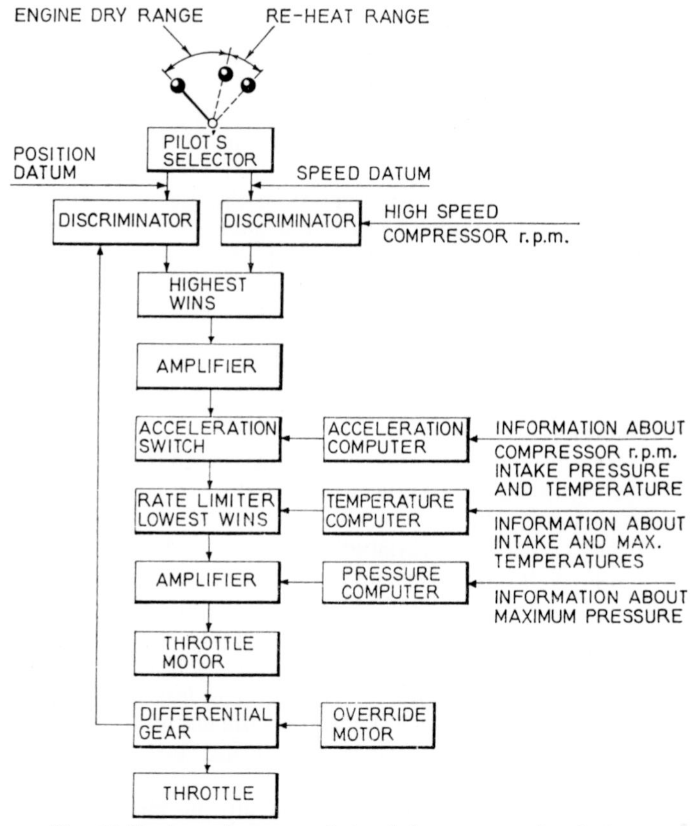

Fig. 67 Basic engine control circuit for two-spool turbojet

tions are better applied at this stage rather than later when the maximum permitted temperature has already been reached.

The nature of the gas turbine, which is open from end to end, is such that a steady build-up of pressure beyond what the compressor can sustain is virtually impossible. In the violent conditions that exist during surge, however, momentary pressure shocks may be applied. If these are sensed by the pressure computer suitable modifications are made to the throttle opening.

99. Propulsion Controls for Supersonic Flight

The very simplest engine control ever to be used in flight consisted of an ignition switch which regulated the power of a piston engine by

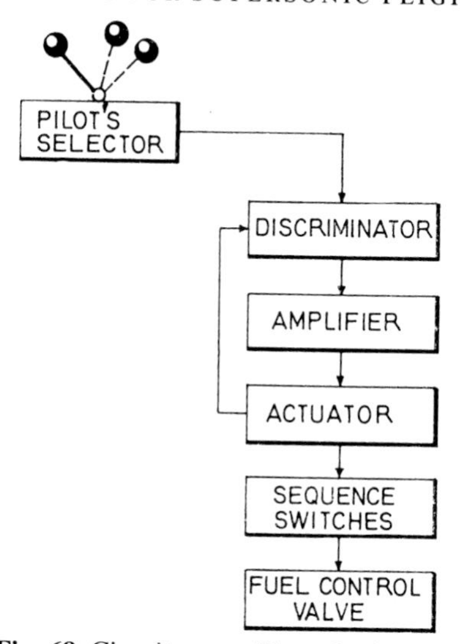

Fig. 68 Circuit controlling afterburner

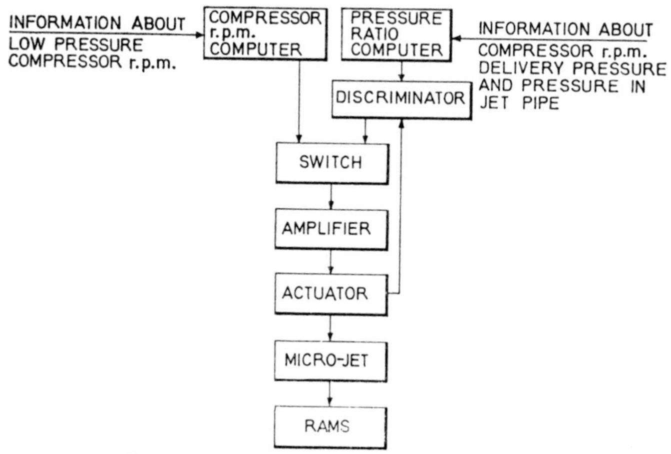

Fig. 69 Circuit controlling variable nozzle

switching on and off as required – a very rough and ready arrangement compared with the layout shown diagrammatically in Fig. 70 for the Concorde powerplant.

There are two main control systems within these powerplants, one

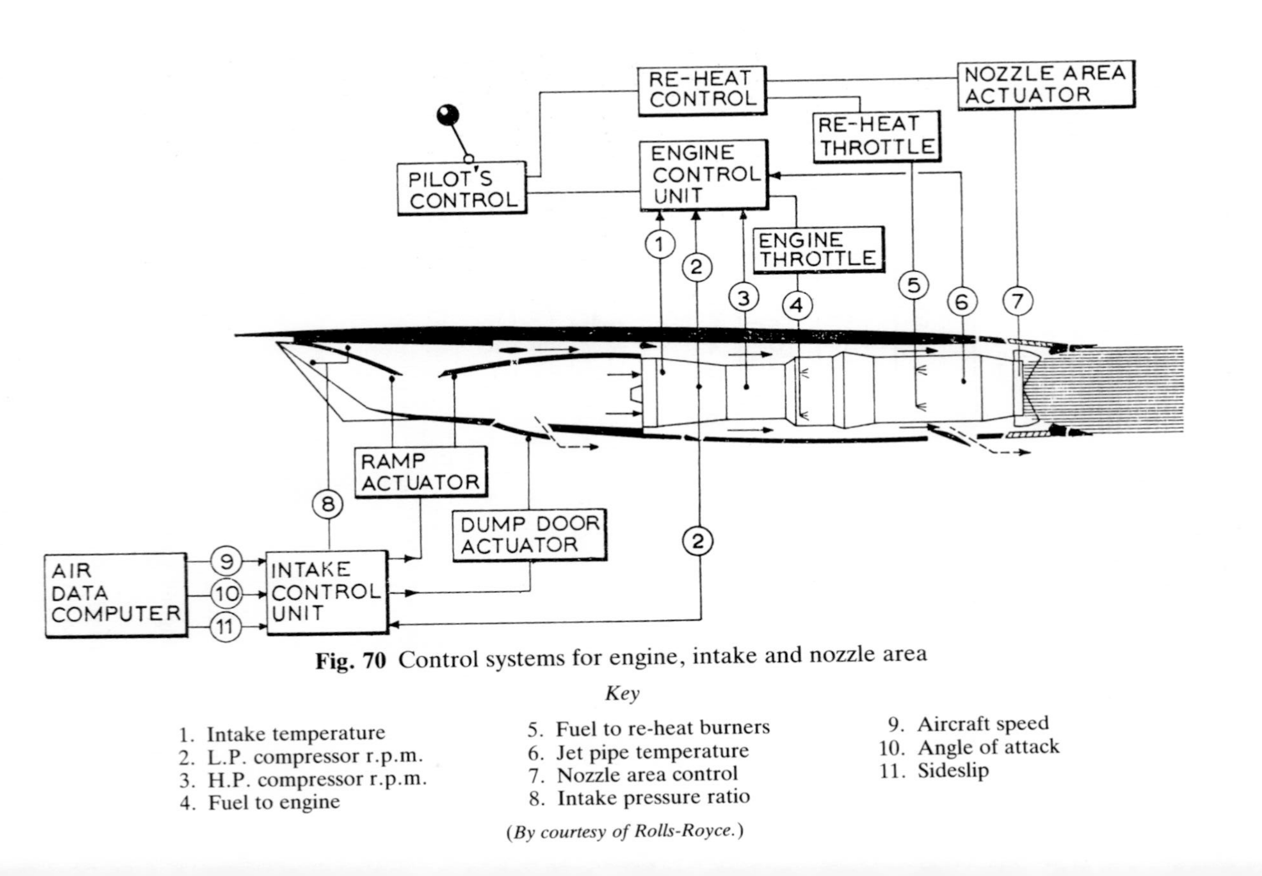

Fig. 70 Control systems for engine, intake and nozzle area

Key

1. Intake temperature
2. L.P. compressor r.p.m.
3. H.P. compressor r.p.m.
4. Fuel to engine
5. Fuel to re-heat burners
6. Jet pipe temperature
7. Nozzle area control
8. Intake pressure ratio
9. Aircraft speed
10. Angle of attack
11. Sideslip

(*By courtesy of Rolls-Royce.*)

deals with the engine and its jet pipe outlet and the other deals with the intake and the variable secondary nozzle.

The engine controls are fairly conventional and follow the lines already established for afterburning engines with the usual safeguards for the prevention of surge, excessive temperatures or troublesome pressures. This particular engine does not need blow-off valves or adjustable inlet guide vanes because of the interconnection that exists between the low-pressure compressor and the adjustable primary nozzle. This arrangement is necessary to avoid excessive temperatures at the turbine inlet arising from the very high temperatures at the compressor inlet when flying at supersonic speeds. It is essential in these circumstances to reduce the work done by the low-pressure compressor (and thus the temperature rise across it) by reducing the mass flow, which is done by closing the primary nozzle. This function differs from the usual one, for the nozzle is normally provided for use during periods in which reheat is in operation.

It will be seen from Fig. 70 that there are two controls which are in no way linked to the throttle motor. These may be regarded as powerplant controls to distinguish them from the engine controls which operate through the throttle. One of these powerplant controls deals with the primary nozzle area; movement is provided by pneumatic rams under the control of a servo mechanism known as a microjet which responds to the pressure ratio across the turbine.

The intake control system is entirely automatic and self-contained; its signals come from a computer which handles information about aircraft speed, attitude and other manoeuvres which influence conditions inside the intake. These, in conjunction with the low-pressure compressor speed, determine the position to be taken up by the ramps and spill doors whose functions have already been mentioned in Section 83.

From what has now been said about controls it will be realized that the scope is a wide one involving many important principles and applications which would occupy a great deal of space if dealt with in detail. The aim of the book has been to give information in a form that may be understood without having recourse to mathematics or too many technicalities; it is hoped that this section on controls may have succeeded in giving some ideas about what the controls are expected to do and how in simple cases the tasks are performed.

100. Conclusion

Engines for aircraft propulsion have always been the subject of rapid technical development. In the case of the piston engine, the power of the largest engines jumped from 100 to 500 h.p. during World War I, then climbed to 1,000 h.p. by the start of World War II and finished that war at the remarkable level of 3,500 h.p. Various Otto-cycle, diesel and compound engines were running by 1953 at powers up to nearly 5,500 h.p., but that was the end. Gas turbines swept away the high-power piston engine, with enormous benefit to aircraft. Not a great deal happened to piston engines for about 30 years. Today, however, air-cooled and liquid-cooled engines operating on the four-stroke or two-stroke cycle are developing rapidly, in sharp competition with such unconventional engines as barrel engines and the RC (rotating-combustion) type. As for gas turbines, these appear capable of delivering any propulsive power needed. Only 20 years ago, when the 747 (Jumbo Jet, the first wide-body) was entering service, 40,000 lb thrust was the limit that could be obtained from a single engine. Today similar engines have reached double this level, with 100,000 lb an assured goal for later in the 1990s. Further comments are offered in the extra section that follows the questionnaire.

The companion volumes in this series finish with a number of questions designed to give the reader a chance of finding out how much he knows. The example is worth following and the questions that are set out below bear the same numbers as the sections of the book on which they are based. Should any difficulty arise in answering a question reference can be made to the appropriate section for the solution. The test is not a difficult one but if you can answer all the questions correctly you may feel like studying the subject further and perhaps even confirming some of the statements that have been made by deriving the necessary formulae yourself.

ONE HUNDRED QUESTIONS

1. (*a*) What is necessary to give lift to the wings of an aircraft?
   (*b*) On what principle does propulsion in a fluid depend?
2. What forces must be equalized by the thrust applied to an aircraft –
   (*a*) In steady horizontal flight?
   (*b*) When climbing at a steady speed?
   (*c*) When accelerating along a level flight path?
3. What are the two main propulsion systems used in aircraft?
4. What are the fundamental differences between propulsion by propeller, jet engine and rocket?
5. Where does the energy come from to give the thrust?
6. What is the best way of keeping down the amount of energy that is inevitably lost when propulsion takes place in a fluid?
7. For what purpose are rockets sometimes used in aircraft which rely on conventional engines for normal flight?
8. What function is common to aerofoils wherever they are used?
9. What is meant by the optimum angle of attack of an aerofoil?
10. (*a*) What two components go to make up the resultant velocity of the air which meets a propeller blade when in flight?
    (*b*) Why is the blade section twisted from root to tip?
11. (*a*) What is the meaning of fine pitch when used in connection with a propeller blade?
    (*b*) When is coarse pitch used?
12. What is the purpose of feathering a propeller blade?
13. For what purpose is the propeller used in reverse pitch?
14. What happens when any portion of a propeller blade travels at a speed in excess of the speed of sound?
15. Why is it usual to run the propeller at about half the speed of the piston engine crankshaft?
16. What fixes the number of blades and their diameter for any given engine power?
17. What are the advantages of the contra-rotating propeller?
18. Why are working conditions worse for the propeller at high altitudes than they are at sea-level?
19. How is speed controlled in propellers fitted with constant-speed mechanisms?
20. (*a*) What do piston engines and gas turbines have in common?
    (*b*) What are the four strokes followed in the engine cycle?

21. What is the purpose of compressing the charge in an engine before combustion takes place?
22. (*a*) Why is the two-stroke engine so called?
    (*b*) What are the meanings of the abbreviations t.d.c. and b.d.c.?
23. (*a*) Why are the valves of four-stroke engines not opened or closed instantaneously?
    (*b*) How much of the heat of the fuel is usefully employed and what happens to the rest of it?
24. Why must poppet-valve mechanisms be kept as light as possible?
25. What advantages do sleeve valves offer compared with poppet valves?
26. What are the advantages of the oversquare engine compared with the long-stroke type?
27. Why are the forces acting on the pistons of a conventional engine greater at t.d.c. than they are at b.d.c.?
28. Why is it desirable to keep crankshafts as short as possible?
29. What does the thrust of a turbojet depend upon?
30. In what way does the turboprop differ from the turbojet?
31. What is the difference between a turboprop and a turbofan?
32. What fundamental difference between piston engines and turbines formerly made it easier to achieve a high efficiency in the former?
33. Why is compression an essential part of the piston engine and gas turbine cycles?
34. Distinguish between compression ratio and pressure ratio.
35. Why is it essential to pump air or mixture into the piston-engine cylinders if there is to be no loss of power at altitude?
36. What features of the centrifugal compressor make it suitable for use on aircraft piston engines?
37. What are the attractions and drawbacks of the exhaust-driven turbine when used to drive a centrifugal supercharger?
38. Why is the two-stage supercharger a more attractive proposition at high altitudes than at sea-level?
39. What is the general principle used in both centrifugal and axial compressors to raise the pressure of the air?
40. How is compression achieved by ram in a forward-facing intake?
41. Why is it so essential to minimize the losses within the intake of a gas turbine?
42. Can a gas turbine continue to run with serious surging in the compressor?
43. What relationship is shown in the series of curves known as compressor characteristics?

44. How does a two-stage centrifugal compressor contribute to a higher engine efficiency than a single-stage compressor?
45. Why has the more elaborate axial compressor almost entirely supplanted the centrifugal compressor in the largest gas turbines?
46. In what respect is the behaviour of the air as it passes between the blades of an axial compressor similar to that of air compressed by ram in a forward-facing intake?
47. What are the conditions of free vortex flow?
48. What are the most marked differences between constant reaction blades and those designed for free vortex flow over their whole length?
49. What happens to the airflow through an axial compressor when the blades stall?
50. What state exists in the airflow through a passage when choking occurs?
51. What is the purpose of the adjustable guide vanes fitted at the entry to some axial compressors?
52. How do blow-off valves contribute to starting an axial compressor?
53. (*a*) In what mechanical respect is the two-spool compressor different from one using only one drum for the blades?
(*b*) What is the main advantage of the two-spool (or three-spool) compressor?
54. Why is it important to avoid excessive temperature rise during compression in a gas turbine?
55. Why is a certain degree of volatility essential in fuels?
56. Why are rich mixtures, which are apparently wasteful, deliberately used for certain running conditions in the piston engine?
57. (*a*) In what respects is detonation different from normal combustion in a piston engine?
(*b*) What quality is expressed in the octane number of a fuel?
58. Why is rapid combustion of the fuel desirable in the aircraft turbine?
59. What essential conditions must be fulfilled before fuel will burn in engine combustion chambers?
60. What is the difference between normally aspirated and supercharged engines?
61. Explain why the pressure drops in the choke of a simple carburettor.
62. What is the purpose of the compensating jets fitted to some carburettors and the diffusers fitted to others?
63. What adjustment must be made to the fuel flow as the aircraft climbs?

64. Why is ice prone to form in aircraft carburettors and what happens if it does?
65. What advantages are obtained by using injectors instead of carburettors?
66. What is the main difference between fuel supply systems using constant-displacement pumps and those using variable-stroke pumps?
67. Why are turbine combustion chambers supplied with air very much in excess of what is needed to burn the fuel?
68. What is the purpose of the swirl vanes at the entry to the combustion chambers?
69. Why is the expansion process in the turbine so much less hazardous than compression?
70. What information is obtained from the transmission dynamometers fitted to certain aircraft engines?
71. What is the advantage of using a large number of small cylinders rather than a smaller number of large cylinders?
72. What energy changes take place during the expansion of hot gases through the turbines and propulsion nozzles?
73. How much energy is extracted from the hot gases by the turbines of: (*a*) a turbojet? (*b*) a turboprop?
74. Why are conditions most critical at the roots of free vortex blades?
75. What combination of factors makes the working conditions of turbine blades very severe?
76. What are the attractions and drawbacks of the radial-flow turbine?
77. What limits the maximum speed available at the outlet from a convergent propulsion nozzle?
78. Why is it possible to boost the thrust of a jet engine by burning fuel in the jet pipe but impossible to burn fuel in the exhaust of a piston engine?
79. What running conditions require the size of the propulsion nozzle to be: (*a*) increased? (*b*) decreased?
80. If a turboprop and a turbojet both give the same thrust at the same speed which is likely to have the higher propulsive efficiency?
81. How can the use of reverse thrust be regarded as a means of improving aircraft performance?
82. Is the pressure increase caused by ram a free gift or has it to be paid for in any way?
83. What are the effects of injecting a mixture of water and methanol at the compressor inlet?

84. Why are pistons and valves so difficult to cool and why is it so important that this should be done properly?
85. Why are automatic controls desirable in engines of high output?
86. (*a*) Why is supercharger control by variable speed devices better than control by throttling?
    (*b*) Name two rather different ways of controlling supercharger speed relative to crankshaft speed.
87. What is the purpose of the automatic boost control?
88. Why are automatic devices used to override the manual control of fuel for the gas turbine?
89. What basic principle is used to limit the maximum speed of turbine shafts?
90. What safeguards are provided by the various pressure-sensitive controls that are used on aircraft turbines?
91. Describe how the air/fuel ratio control and the pressure ratio switch act to prevent surge.
92. Why are the highest possible temperatures and pressures used at the turbine entry?
93. Describe the sequence of events involved in bringing afterburning (reheat) into use.
94. What are the advantages of electrically operated controls compared with those which rely on mechanical linkages or on hydraulic systems?
95. What are the difficulties involved in measuring jet pipe temperature?
96. Explain how electrical control between the pilot's lever and the throttle motor is used to give protection from surge when the pilot's lever is moved too quickly.
97. Why do automatic controls concern themselves with the rate at which speed and temperature rise as well as with the actual values of these two quantities?
98. Why does the Concorde propulsion unit require a variable primary nozzle in the jet pipe even when reheat is not in use?
99. Why is a convergent nozzle used at subsonic speed but a divergent one at supersonic speed, in each case to accelerate the propulsive jet?
100. What level of thrust will the most powerful engines reach by the year 2000?

The past twenty years

Anyone in possession of the original edition of this book will appreciate that the text has been almost completely rewritten, but much still remains to be added. Certainly many things have happened that could not be predicted at the end of the 1960s.

One thing that was predictable was the disappearance of the large piston engine, apart from the fields of agricultural aviation and fire bombing. Both duties take place at the minimum safe height above ground level, where the gas turbine is less efficient. Moreover, many of the fire bombers are converted bombers or ocean-patrol aircraft, available at capital cost perhaps one-tenth that of a new purpose-built machine. Remarkably, all these remaining high-power piston engines are of basic designs which can be traced straight back to about 1925, and little changed since 1945.

In 1969 in the giant market of engines for light aircraft there was a virtual 100 per cent monopoly enjoyed by horizontally opposed air-cooled engines made by two US manufacturers, Continental and Lycoming. Today competition is appearing from all sides. Around 1975 it became apparent that there was much to be said for car engines, which instead of being massive and cumbersome were actually fully competitive on the score of weight and often better in first cost, smoothness, quietness, economy, low emissions and reliability (Plate 7). One result is that many of the latest Continental engines are water- (or glycol-water) cooled. For ultralights and microlights no fewer than 95 makes of very attractive piston engine are available, often with a weight of less than 1 lb/h.p. complete with starter/generator and silencer.

New species of engine include the barrel and the RC. By far the best known RC (rotating-combustion) type is the Wankel, and while this made only a limited penetration of the car market it is thrusting firmly into the field of microlights, target drones, reconnaissance vehicles and other unmanned and manned applications (Plate 10). These engines are based on a kind of piston-engine cycle of compression, ignition and exhaust within spaces sealed between a rotating triangle with slightly bulged sides and a surrounding space looking slightly like a figure 8. RC engines can be perfectly balanced and run at extremely high speed and, remarkably, with high efficiency.

As for the barrel engine, this does have pistons oscillating in cylinders, but the latter are double-ended and arranged inside a large cylindrical block with their axes parallel to that of the main cylinder (Plates 11 and 12). The pistons drive the sloping surfaces of a kind of zigzag cam wheel which in turn drives the output shaft. In today's

Dyna-Cam, which has been intermittently developed for 60 years, six double-ended pistons give smooth propulsion at a modest 2,000 r.p.m., the power being 250 h.p., with good fuel economy and with very few moving parts. Clearly, we can expect plenty of new forms of piston engine.

Turning to gas turbines, a basic change is the elimination of the turbojet except from the smallest and simplest applications, such as target drones and cruise missiles. Fighters now have turbofans with BPR in the region of 1 (Plate 16), and invariably with an afterburner, though the sudden emergence of stealth as a crucial factor in survival makes actual use of an afterburner (at least in hostile territory) highly undesirable. Such aircraft as the F-117A and B-2 bombers and F-22A fighter (Plate 19) have special nozzles, the first two designed purely for minimal observability and the F-22A nozzle being of two-dimensional (rectangular) form with variable flaps to give limited thrust vectoring for enhanced manoeuvrability. Such nozzles have been tested with an added reverse-thrust capability, but in the case of the F-22A this was not asked for (odd, in view of the vulnerability of airfields).

All transports, military airlifters, business jets and airliners of all sizes, are powered by engines which work on the largest possible airflow. For speeds up to 400 knots the turboprop (Plate 14) is preferred, using lightweight low-noise propellers with five or six blades. For speeds around 500 knots (575 m.p.h.) the propfan is becoming important in the Soviet Union. Such engines were developed by Western companies from 1979 onwards (Plates 29 and 30), but work then dwindled as the price of fuel began to fall. The logical Russians said 'If an engine burns less fuel, it is sensible to develop it anyway, because we cannot replace the fuel we burn. You in the West would do well to pick up the propfan where you left it off'. Examples of Soviet propfans are the D-27 and NK-93. The Lotarev D-27 is rated at about 13,900 h.p., with fuel economy 25 per cent below the best turbofans. For such aircraft as the Antonov An-180 its contra-rotating scimitar propellers are ahead of the engine, as a tractor. For the Yak-46 it would be reversed, as a pusher. This would be quieter, but will be about three years later. The Kuznetsov NK-93 is bigger, rated at 39,680 lb thrust. The basic core has a 7-stage LP compressor and 8-stage HP, giving an overall pressure ratio of 37. A three-stage turbine drives a differential planetary gearbox to the contra-rotating scimitar fans, the front having eight sharp-edged blades and the rear ten. BPR is 16.6, the diameter being 114 in and weight 8,047 lb. Unlike the D-27 the NK-93 blades are inside a long-chord duct, which at the cost of extra weight gives higher propulsive efficiency and reduced noise.

Conventional turbofans naturally continue to develop with ever higher pressure ratio and TET (turbine entry temperature), to give thrusts up to 100,000 lb. The three great rivals, Pratt & Whitney, General Electric and Rolls-Royce, each think they have the best engines, and are hard at work fitting bigger and bigger fans. Certainly Rolls-Royce has led with fan technology, replacing numerous slender and heavy titanium blades by a much smaller number of broad blades with no part-span snubbers. At one stroke this has dramatically reduced engine weight, increased thrust and improved specific fuel consumption. The gains are manifest in increased thrust from a given fan diameter. The original Pratt & Whitney JT9D gave 40,000 lb from a fan of 95.6 in diameter. Today about 70,000 lb can be reached by this size of fan (Plate 23), and with a 120-in fan the magic 100,000 lb thrust is in sight. BPR for these super-powerful engines is in the range from 7 to 12. Thus, aircraft designers can pick engines with any BPR from zero (i.e., the turbojet) up to about 50 (the turboprop). It is just remarkable that it has taken so long.

INDEX

Plate 1. A space rocket
The Rocketdyne SSME (Space Shuttle Main Engine) is the first space rocket to be designed for repeated use, with airline-type maintenance between flights. A single SSME is seen on test. The Shuttle Orbiter has three, giving a thrust above the atmosphere of 1,466,400 lb, burning liquid oxygen and liquid hydrogen at 3,300°C. The nozzle diameter is 94 in.

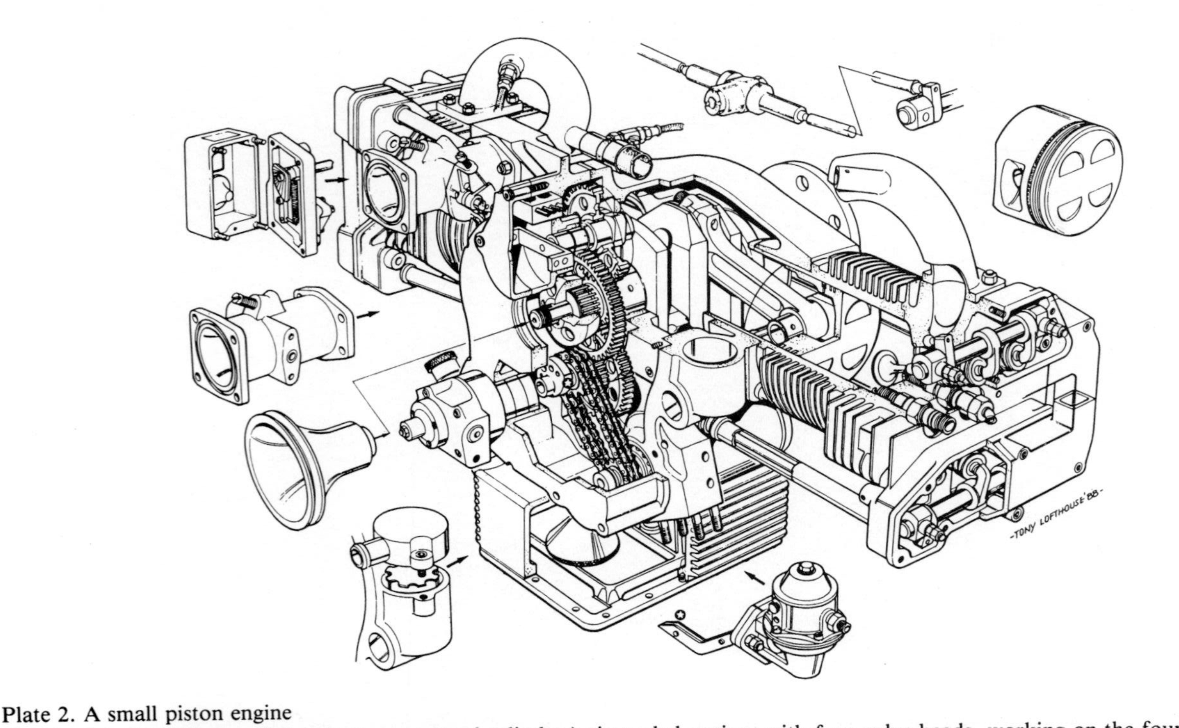

Plate 2. A small piston engine
The Emdair CF Series are flat-twin (two opposed cylinders) air-cooled engines with four-valve heads, working on the four-stroke cycle. They come in different sizes giving 60 to 85 h.p., typically weighing just over 100 lb. In this drawing the propeller drive is on the far (right) side.

Plate 3. Sportplane engine
Rotax of Austria is the world's biggest supplier of engines for microlights and other sporting aircraft. The engine shown is the Type 503, with two air-cooled two-stroke cylinders with piston-port valves, each fed by its own carburettor. Complete with these and the big exhaust system seen at the top it weighs 79 lb, and is rated at 51 h.p. at 6,500 r.p.m.

Plate 4. A liquid-cooled engine
The Teledyne Continental Voyager T-550 is a six-cylinder engine of 300 h.p. designed for the re-engined Beech Bonanza. It has direct drive, and a turbocharger driven by the exhaust gas (visible at lower right). On top are the fine pipes through which fuel is injected into the cylinders.

Plate 5. Liquid-cooled aircraft
Thanks to its 350 h.p. Voyager 550A engines and beautiful streamlining the RAM/Cessna 414AW can cruise on only 75 per cent power at 281 mph at a startling 30,000 ft. Hardly visible above the trailing edge is one of the air inlets to the cooling radiators (see next plate).

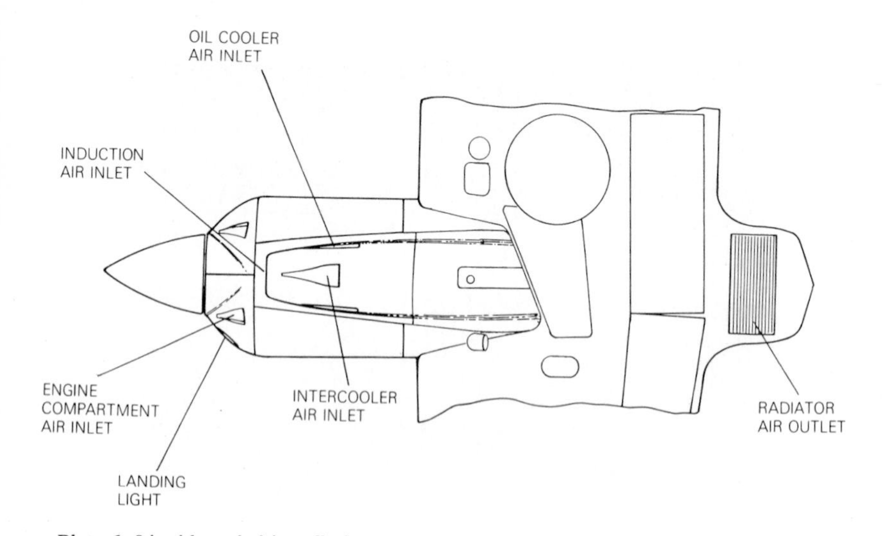

Plate 6. Liquid-cooled installation
Looking up at the right-hand engine of a RAM/Cessna 414AW. The coolant mixture (60 per cent Prestone glycol antifreeze and 40 per cent water) is pumped through a radiator inside the shallow tail of the nacelle behind the wing.

Plate 7. A converted car engine
In recent years it has been realised that modern car engines can form the basis for outstanding aviation engines. This example, flown in a French Robin 3140 in 1983, is the V-6 engine of 180/200 h.p. used in Peugeot, Renault and Volvo cars. For aircraft use it has a wide belt reduction gear (visible).

Plate 8. An American diesel
The In-Tech Merlyn is a three-cylinder inline turbocharged two stroke. Capacity is only 210 cu in (3.47 litres) and weight 580 lb, yet takeoff power is 650 h.p. at 4,800 r.p.m.

Plate 9. A Russian diesel
This full-size mock-up shows the appearance of the DN-200, DN standing for Diesel Novikov. Aleksandr S. Novikov, chief designer of the huge Rybinsk machine-building factory, wanted to build the most efficient engine for light aircraft. The DN.200 has six opposed pistons in three horizontal cylinders, driving a crankshaft along each side. At the front are the auxiliaries and propeller shaft, and at the rear is the turbocharger. This 200 h.p. engine will weigh 364 lb, and should fly in 1995.

Plate 10. An RC engine
Rotating-combustion (Wankel type) engines are popular in small sizes. This British example, the Norton NR801, has a single rotor with liquid-cooled housings. Complete with generator and silencer it weighs 50 lb, and it gives 52 h.p. at 7,500 r.p.m.

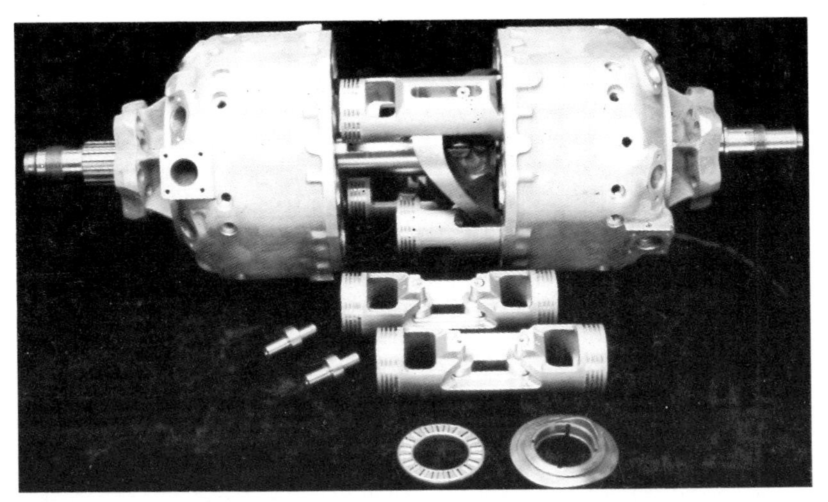

Plate 11. A barrel engine
The Dyna-Cam is 40 in long and 13 in diameter, weighs 300 lb and develops 250 h.p. Here the engine is opened to reveal how the six double-ended pistons drive the rotating cam in the centre of the engine.

Plate 12. A barrel engine installed
This Dyna-Cam has been flight tested in a Piper Arrow, enhancing the rate of climb. With the cowling off one can see the long exhaust pipes and small radiator.

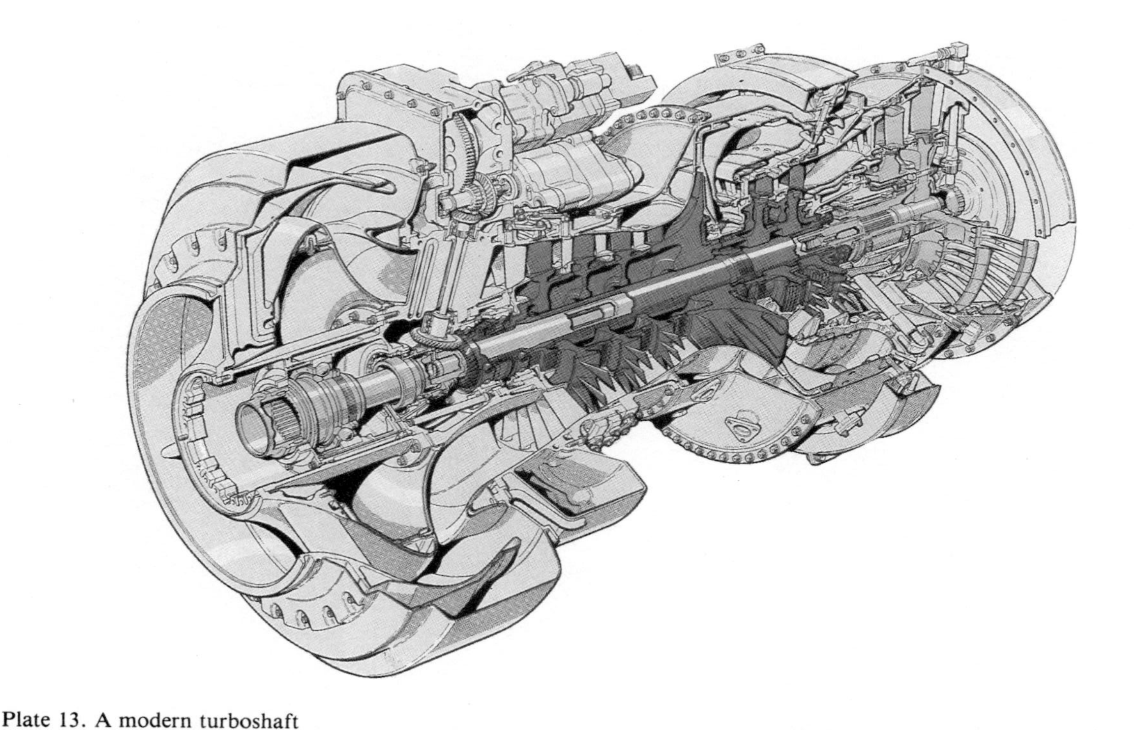

Plate 13. A modern turboshaft
Turboshaft engines drive helicopters and some other VTOL (vertical takeoff and landing) aircraft. The Rolls-Royce Turbomeca RTM 322 has a compressor with three axial stages and one centrifugal, driven by a two-stage turbine. A second two-stage turbine drives the output shaft down the centre. This 2,400 h.p. engine weighs 538 lb.

Plate 14. A modern turboprop
The Allison GMA 2100A is a 6,100 h.p. engine, but for the Saab 2000 it is derated to a maximum of 4,152 s.h.p., flat-rated to 37°C. The Dowty six-blade propeller is driven by the remote gearbox carried high ahead of the engine, with accessories on its rear face.

Plate 15. Afterburner burners
With the complete jetpipe removed this Soviet Tumanskii R-29B fighter turbojet (made under licence in India) reveals its array of afterburner spray rings and radial pipes, the flames from which are stabilized by the prominent gutter rings. When reheat is selected each ring lights up in sequence, smoothly augmenting sea-level thrust from 17,635 lb to 27,500 lb.

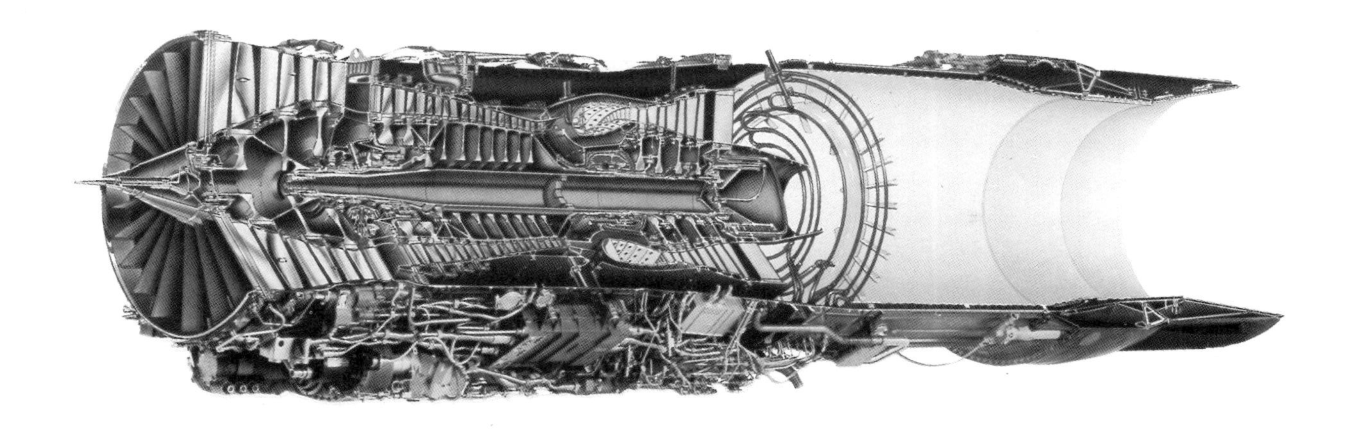

Plate 16. A fighter engine
Typical of 1980-style fighter engines, the Pratt & Whitney F100-229 IPE (Improved Performance Engine) goes into the latest F-15s and F-16s, with a rating of 29,000 lb for a weight of 3,650 lb. In such engines the bypassed air from the LP compressor provides a large excess of oxygen to support combustion in the afterburner, whose spray rings and bars are all in the same plane.

Plate 17. A vectored-thrust engine
The Soviet Tumanskii R-27V turbojet powers the Yak-38 V/STOL (vertical or short takeoff and landing) naval aircraft. The jetpipe forms a plenum chamber from which the gas escapes through two nozzles which can be vectored to the rear or (as seen here) downwards by rotating through 95°. Thrust is 15,300 lb.

Plate 18. A supersonic ventral inlet
The British EAP (Experimental Aircraft Programme) demonstrator is powered by two RB. 199 turbofans fed from a prominent rectangular inlet under the forward fuselage. In many ways the inlet resembles that of Concorde, though the lower lip is hinged.

Plate 19. Supersonic lateral inlets
At the end of the century the US Air Force will begin deploying squadrons of Lockheed F-22 fighters, a prototype of which is seen here head-on. The inlets are a compromise between the need for high efficiency, even in violent manoevres, and minimum radar signature. The thick black lines separating them from the fuselage are the gaps through which the boundary layer is rejected, part escaping through the grilles in the top of the wing. The ducts curve sharply inwards, partly to hide the engines from enemy radars and partly to leave room for internal missile bays on each side of the aircraft.

Plate 20. Concorde nozzles
Illustrated diagramatically in the text, the nozzles of Concorde terminate in unusual downstream secondary nozzles formed by just two parts, upper and lower. The engine at left is in cruise (supersonic expansion), while that at right is in takeoff (the jet squeezed slightly to reduce noise). After landing, the two clamshells swing round to block off the jet to reverse the thrust. Here, both primary nozzles are closed.

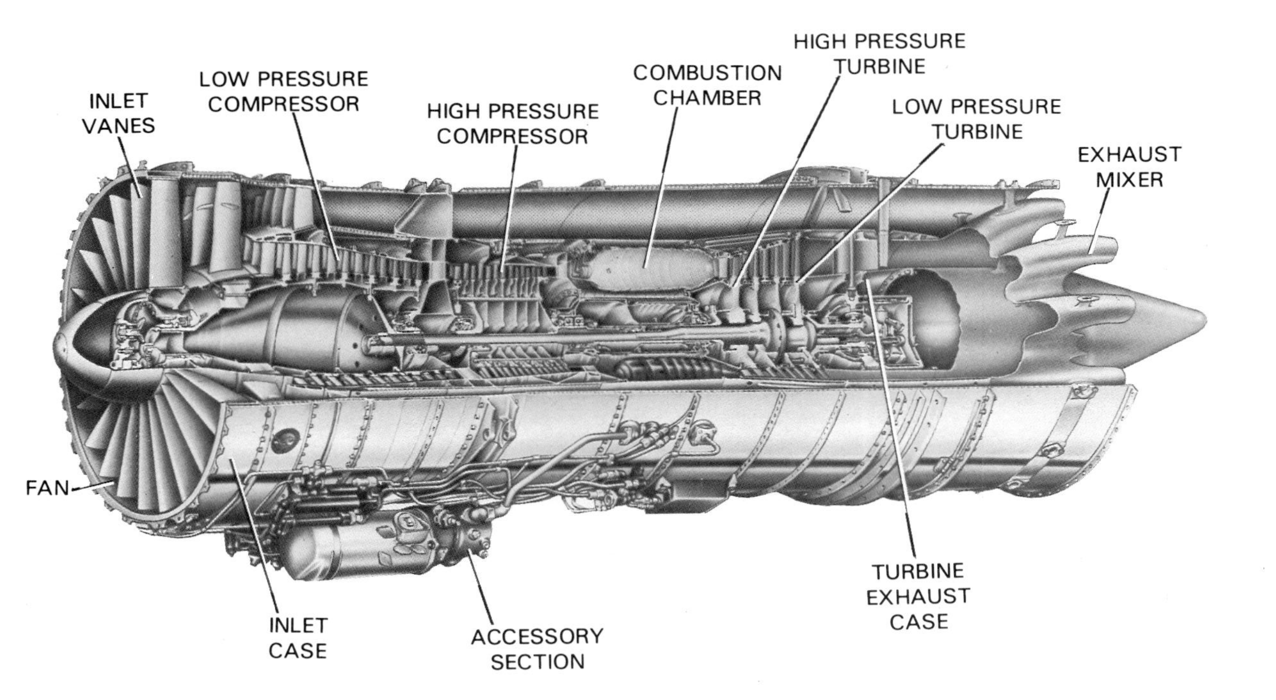

Plate 21. A traditional turbofan
The world's most widely used airline engine is the Pratt & Whitney JT8D, a turbofan of LBPR (low bypass ratio) type. Even this refanned JT8D-200 version has a BPR well below 1.8, with inlet vanes upsteam of the narrow-blade fan. But it does have a mixer nozzle, partly to reduce noise and also to improve efficiency. JT8D engines power DC-9, MD-80 and 737 aircraft at 14,000 to 21,000 lb thrust.

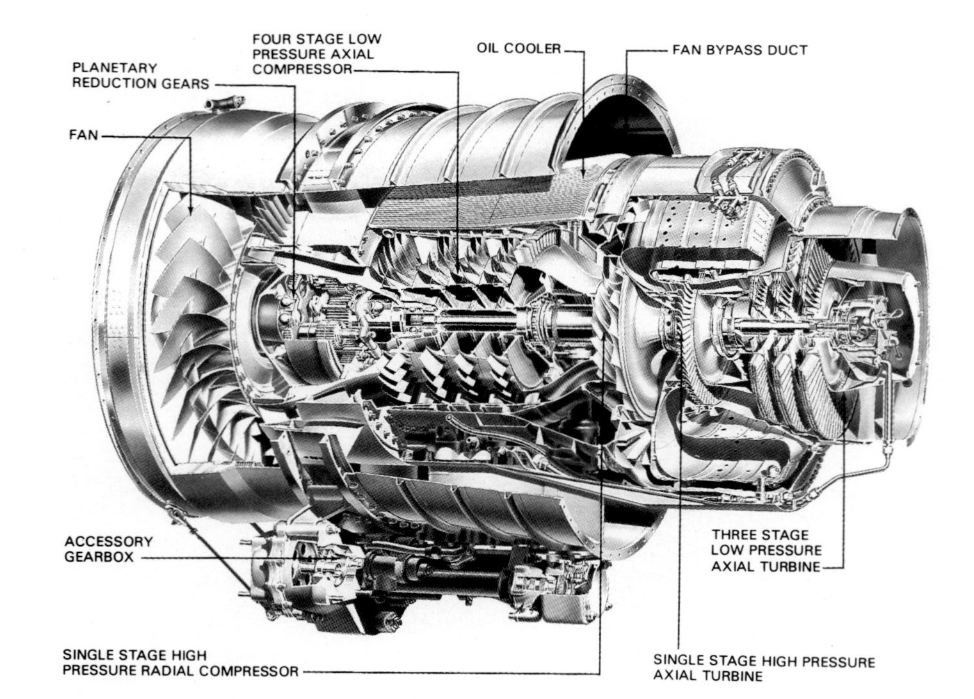

Plate 22. A bizjet engine. The Garrett TFE731 is the world's most widely used business-jet engine, and it also powers military trainers, at ratings from 3,500 to 4,500 lb. The HP turbine drives the centrifugal (here called radial) compressor only. The three-stage LP turbine drives the LP compressor and, via a reduction gear, the fan. The combustion chamber is folder back around the turbines.

Plate 23. A wide-body engine
The Pratt & Whitney PW4000 is typical of today's high-BPR turbofans in the 50,000-70,000 lb thrust class. It has a traditional fan with 38 slender blades of solid titanium with part-span shrouds (snubbers), clearly seen here. The rings round the turbine section are HP air pipes for active clearance control (see Fig. 53).

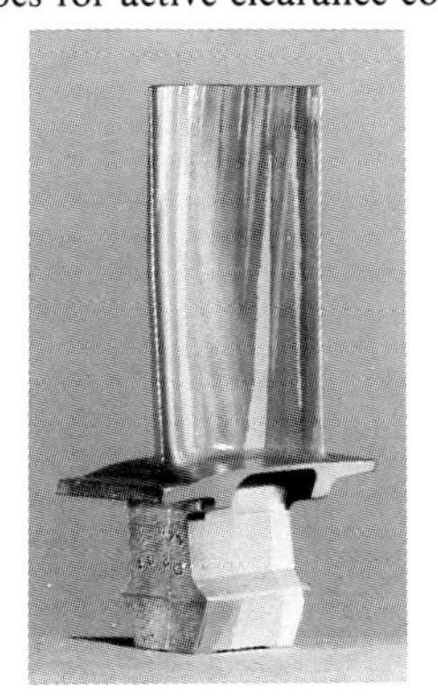

Conventional

Directional solidification

Single crystal

Plate 24. Modern turbine blades
These photographs show the three ways in which turbine rotor blades are made. Each is shown as-cast, before any machining, with the surface etched to reveal grain structure. The traditional cast blade shows a random grain structure. The DS blade has all grains arranged longitudinally. The SC blade has no weak inter-grain boundaries at all.

Plate 25. Fan ducts
The Air France Airbus 320 has CFM56 engines with short fan ducts, the core engine being visible downstream. The Indian A320 has V2500 engines with full-length fan ducts, terminating in large mixer nozzles with reversers.

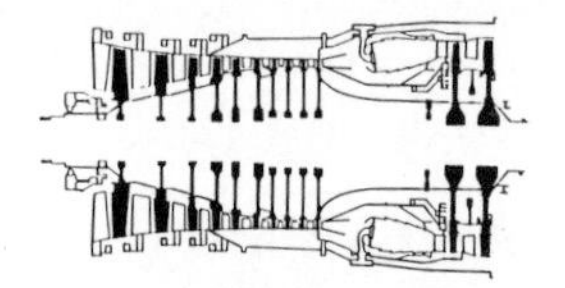

BR 700 core
Launch in march 1991

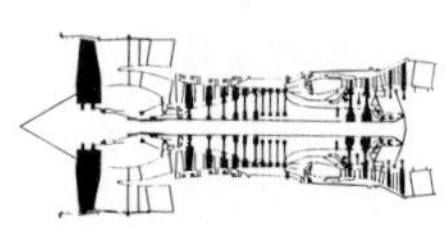

BR 710 Turbofan
8,000 - 12,000 lbf, 40″ fan

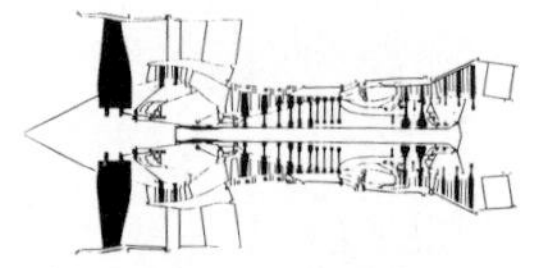

BR 715 Turbofan
14,000 - 18,000 lbf, 53″ fan

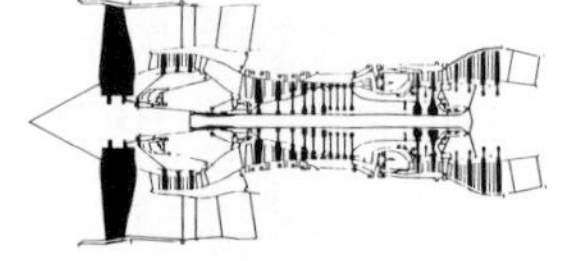

BR 720 Turbofan
18,000 - 22,000 lbf, 55″ fan

Plate 26. An engine family
Having developed an efficient HP core, which is the hardest part, manufacturers like to use it in turboshaft, turboprop, turbofan and even propfan engines, if they can. Here BMW Rolls-Royce show how they intend to use the same core in turbofans of three thrust levels, with different sizes of fan and different numbers of LP compressor and LP turbine stages.

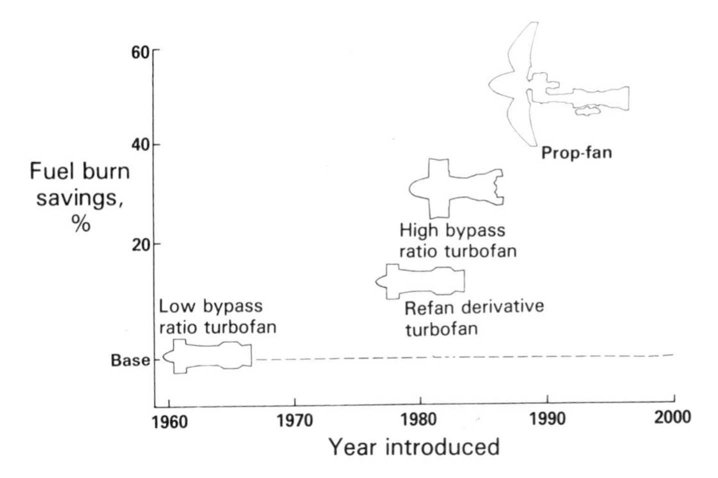

Plate 27. The transport engine spectrum
These sketches show approximately how fuel burn in airliners of the 80-200 seat class can be reduced by introducing more efficient propulsion systems. The LBPR baseline engine might be the JT8D, and the refan the JT8D-200 version or Rolls-Royce Tay. The HBPR engine could be the CFM56 or V2500. No propfan was introduced in 1990, because (perhaps shortsightedly) work relaxed when fuel prices began to fall.

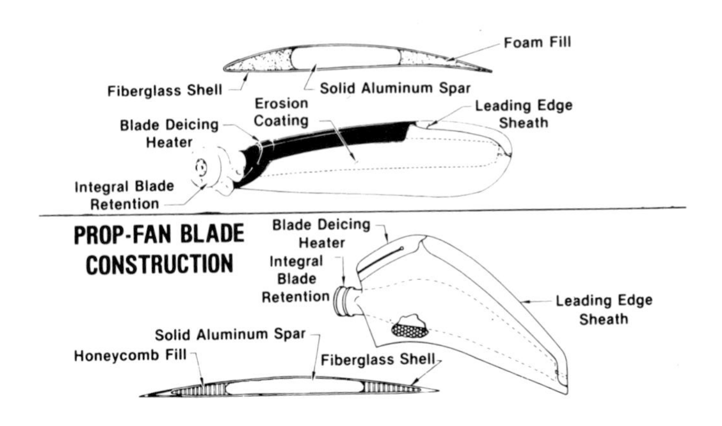

Plate 28. Propeller and propfan blades
These diagrams are based on the technology of an American company, Hamilton Standard, which prefers to use a single aluminium spar to which are attached low-density leading and trailing portions. Apart from the totally different shape the propfan blade is thinner, sharper-edged and has honeycomb fill instead of foam.

Plate 29. A propfan
One of the more unusual propfans is General Electric's UDF (unducted fan) engine. As its name implies, the contra-rotating fan blades are not surrounded by a duct. There is no gearbox, the external propulsor blades being driven by large multi-stage contra-rotating turbines in the internal gas steam. BPR is 36, and thrust in the 25,000 lb class. See final Plate.

Plate 30. A propfan airliner
The UDF engine (Plate 29) first flew on a Boeing 727 in August 1986. In May 1987 it powered this MD-80. As the fast-rotating propulsor blades are not very prominent the engine does not look very different from the turbofan previously fitted, but the sound and behaviour of the variable-pitch blades was totally different.